HOUGHTON MIFFLIN LITERARY READERS

BOOK 3

HOUGHTON MIFFLIN COMPANY   BOSTON

Atlanta   Dallas   Geneva, Illinois   Palo Alto   Princeton   Toronto

Program Authors

William K. Durr, John J. Pikulski, Rita M. Bean, J. David Cooper, Nicholas A. Glaser, M. Jean Greenlaw, Hugh Schoephoerster, Mary Lou Alsin, Kathryn Au, Rosalinda B. Barrera, Joseph E. Brzeinski, Ruth P. Bunyan, Jacqueline C. Comas, Frank X. Estrada, Robert L. Hillerich, Timothy G. Johnson, Pamela A. Mason, Joseph S. Renzulli

Senior Consultants

Jacqueline L. Chaparro, Alan N. Crawford, Alfredo Schifini, Sheila Valencia

Program Reviewers

Donna Bessant, Mara Bommarito, Yetive Bradley, Patricia M. Callan, Clara J. Hanline, Fannie Humphery, Barbara H. Jeffus, Beverly Jimenez, Sue Cramton Johnson, Michael P. Klentschy, Petra Montante, Nancy Rhodes, Julie Ryan, Lily Sarmiento, Ellis Vance, Judy Williams, Leslie M. Woldt, Janet Gong Yin

Acknowledgments

For each of the selections listed below, grateful acknowledgment is made for permission to adapt and/or reprint original or copyrighted material, as follows:

"Annie and the Old One," by Miska Miles. Text copyright © 1971 by Miska Miles. Reprinted by permission of Little, Brown and Company.

"Brave Janet Reachfar," by Jane Duncan. Text copyright © 1975 by Jane Duncan. Reprinted by permission of Clarion Books/Ticknor and Fields (a Houghton Mifflin company) and Macmillan London Limited.

"The Buried Treasure," entire text from the book by Djemma Bider. Copyright © 1982 by Djemma Bider. Reprinted by permission of Dodd, Mead, and Company, Inc.

"Digging Up Dinosaurs," by Aliki Brandenberg (Thomas Y. Crowell). Copyright © 1981 by Aliki Brandenberg. Reprinted by permission of Harper and Row, Publishers, Inc.

"Dragon Stew," text copyright © 1969 by Tom McGowen. Reprinted by permission of the author.

"Dreams," from *The Dream Keeper and Other Poems* by Langston Hughes. Copyright © 1932 by Alfred A. Knopf, Inc., and renewed 1960 by Langston Hughes. Reprinted by permission of Alfred A. Knopf, Inc.

Continued on page 406.

Contents

Houghton Mifflin Literature
Pourquoi Tales

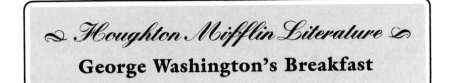

Houghton Mifflin Literature
George Washington's Breakfast

5.   Journeys

Houghton Mifflin Literature
Warton and the King of the Skies

6. Learning Lessons

Houghton Mifflin Literature
Fables

7. Clever Ideas

Animal
Wonders

The White Stallion

by Elizabeth Shub
Illustrated by Rachel Isadora

This is a true story, Gretchen. My grandmother Gretchen, your great-great-grandmother, told it to me. She was as young as you are when it happened. She was as old as I am when I heard it from her.

It was 1845. Three families were on their way West. They planned to settle there. They traveled in covered wagons. Each wagon was drawn by four horses. Conestoga wagons they were called.

Gretchen and her family were in the last wagon. Mother and Father sat on the driver's seat. The children were inside with the household goods. Bedding, blankets, pots and pans, a table, chairs, a dresser took up most of the space. There was not much room left for Trudy, John, Billy, and Gretchen. Gretchen was the youngest.

Behind the wagon walked Anna, their old mare. She was not tied to the wagon but followed faithfully. She carried two sacks of corn meal on her back.

It was hot in the noonday sun. The children were cranky and bored. The wagon cover shaded them, but little air came in through the openings at front and back. John kicked Billy. Billy pushed him, and he bumped Gretchen. Trudy, the oldest, who was trying to read, scolded them. Their quarrel was interrupted by Father's voice.

"Quick, everybody, look out! There's a herd of mustangs."

The children clambered to the back of the wagon. In the distance they could see the wild horses. The horses galloped swiftly and, in minutes, were out of sight.

"Look at Anna," John said.

The old mare stood rigid. She had turned her head toward the mustangs. Her usually floppy ears were lifted high. The wagon had moved some distance before Anna trotted after it.

It was hotter than ever inside. "Father," Gretchen called, "may I ride on Anna for a while?"

Father stopped the wagon and came to the back. He lifted Gretchen onto the mare. The meal sacks made a comfortable seat. He tied her securely so that she would not fall off. As they moved on, Gretchen fell asleep, lulled by the warmth of the sun.

They were following a trail in Texas along the Guadalupe River. The rear wheel of the first wagon hit a boulder, and the axle broke. The whole train stopped. Anna strayed away, with Gretchen sleeping on her back. No one noticed.

The travelers made camp. Children were sent for firewood and for water from the river. The women prepared food. It was not until the axle had been fixed and they were ready to eat that Gretchen and Anna were missed.

The men tried to follow the mare's tracks but soon lost them. It was getting dark. There was nothing to do but remain where they were. They would search again at the first sign of light. Faithful Anna, they thought, would return. She probably had discovered a rich patch of mesquite grass. She would come back when she had eaten all she wanted.

Gretchen awoke to the sound of lapping. Anna
was drinking noisily from a stream. A short distance
away stood a herd of ten or twelve wild horses. They
were brownish in color. Some had darker brown
stripes down their backs. Others had dark markings
on their legs. They were mares.

After Anna had finished drinking, she moved
toward them. And they walked forward as if to greet
her. When they came close, they neighed and nick-
ered. They crossed necks with Anna, nuzzled her and
rubbed against her. They were so friendly that

Gretchen was not afraid. And she did not realize that Anna had wandered far from the wagon train.

Suddenly the horses began to nibble at the sacks on Anna's back. They had smelled the corn meal. In their eagerness they nipped Gretchen's legs. Gretchen screamed. She tried to move out of the way. She tried to loosen the ropes that tied her. But she could not reach the knots. Terrified, Gretchen screamed and screamed.

Out of nowhere a great white stallion appeared. He pranced and whinnied. He swished his long white tail. He stood on his hind legs, his white mane flying.

The mares moved quickly out of his way. The white stallion came up to Anna. He carefully bit through the ropes that tied Gretchen. Then, gently, he took hold of the back of her dress with his teeth. He lifted her to the ground. He seemed to motion to

the mares with his head, and then he galloped away. The mares followed at once. Anna followed them.

Gretchen was left alone. She did not know what to do. "Father will find me soon," she said out loud to comfort herself. She was hungry, but there was nothing to eat. She walked to the stream and drank some water. Then she sat down on a rock to wait.

She waited and waited, but there was no sign of Father. And no sign of Anna. Shadows began to fall. The sun went down. The dark came.

"Anna!" Gretchen called. "Anna! Anna! Anna!" There was no answering sound.

She heard a coyote howl. She heard the rustling of leaves and the call of redbirds. Gretchen began to cry. She made a place for herself on some dry leaves near a tree trunk. She curled up against it, and cried and cried until she fell asleep.

Morning light woke Gretchen. The stream sparkled in the sunlight. Gretchen washed her face and drank the clear water. She looked for Anna. She called her name, but Anna did not come. Gretchen was so hungry she chewed some sweet grass. But it had a nasty taste, and she spat it out. She sat on her rock near the stream. She looked at the red bite marks on her legs and began to cry again.

A squirrel came by. It looked at her in such a funny way that she stopped crying. She walked along the stream. She knew she must not go far. "If you are lost," Mother had warned, "stay where you are. That will make it easier to find you." Gretchen walked back to her rock.

It was afternoon when she heard the sound of hooves. A moment later Anna ambled up to the stream. The sacks of meal were gone.

The old mare drank greedily. Gretchen hugged and kissed her. She patted her back. Anna would find her way back to the wagon train.

She tried to climb on Anna's back, but even without the sacks the mare was too high. There was a fallen tree not far away. Gretchen wanted to use it as a step. She tugged at Anna, but Anna would not move. Gretchen pulled and shoved. She begged and pleaded. Anna stood firm.

Now again the white stallion appeared. Again he lifted Gretchen by the back of her dress. He sat her on Anna's back. He nuzzled and pushed the old mare. Anna began to walk. The white stallion walked close behind her for a few paces. Then, as if to say goodbye, he stood on his hind legs, whinnied, and galloped away.

Gretchen always believed the white stallion had told Anna to take her back to the wagon train. For that is what Anna did.

Your great-great-grandmother Gretchen bore the scars of the wild mare bites for the rest of her life. I know because when she told me the story, she pulled down her stockings. And I saw them.

Author

Elizabeth Shub, who knows several languages, has translated and retold many old tales, among them *Clever Kate* from the Brothers Grimm. She worked with the prize-winning author Isaac Singer on many of his books. *The White Stallion* is an old Western legend that she has retold. It was chosen as a Notable Book of 1982 by the American Library Association.

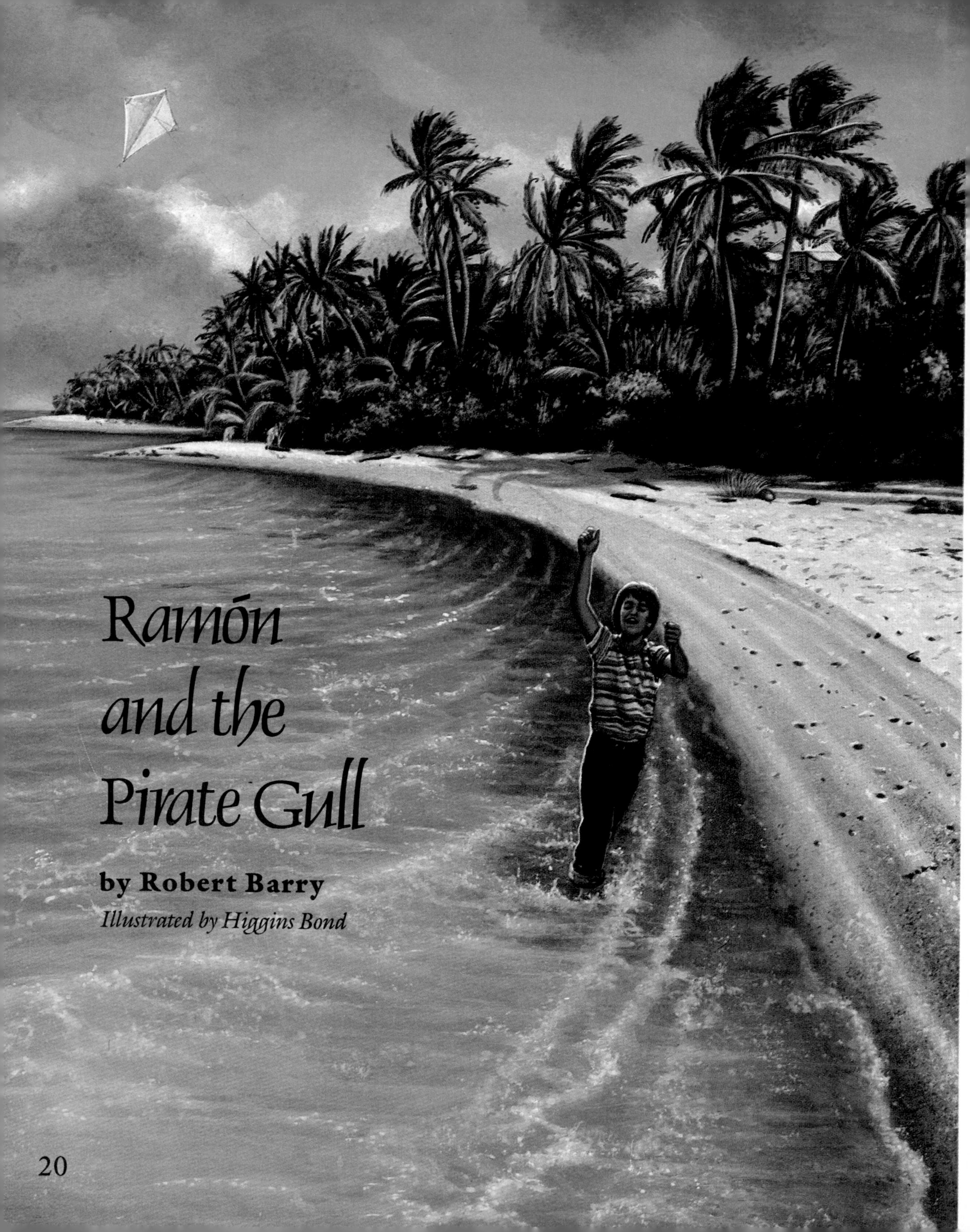

Ramón
and the
Pirate Gull

by Robert Barry

Illustrated by Higgins Bond

Ramón's kite rose higher and higher in the morning sky. He let the string slip slowly through his fingers, as he stood on the beach in the soft, drowsy warmth of the morning sun. He closed his eyes. Even without looking, he could tell by the string's pull on his hand when the kite was tossing to the left or to the right, and when it was about to swoop and slice a big circle in the bright Caribbean sky.

Suddenly, a strange, laughing sound pierced the air. *Haah, haah, haah* . . . Ramón opened his eyes. He blinked them at a bright flash of red. High overhead a bird posed briefly, then dove straight down at a pelican fishing lazily in the waters of the bay.

The bird landed lightly on the pelican's head. Ramón gasped. IT WAS A BRIGHT RED GULL! At just the right moment, when the big bird opened its huge beak, the gull darted in with his head and speared a fish out of the pelican's pouch. Then it sailed away into the sky.

Ramón held his breath with amazement as the red gull came back again and again to perch on the pelican's head and snatch more fish. Ramón counted two, four, five, six fish!

At last there was only one fish left in the pelican's pouch. Gull and pelican fought a brief tug-of-war. The gull won. Swiftly it flew away with its prize, disappearing over the palm trees that lined the edge of the beach.

Ramón shook his head and hauled in his kite as quickly as he could. He ran along the path overhung with tangled sea grapes to the clearing where his house stood.

"A sea gull . . . a sea gull as red as a ruby. I saw it at the beach," he cried.

"What are you shouting about, Ramón?" his mother asked, coming out onto the porch. "You know that sea gulls are not red. Maybe you saw a crane. I have seen pictures of pink ones with long legs."

"Yes, it's true," Ramón insisted and tried to catch his breath. "I saw a red sea gull stealing fish from a pelican . . . just like a pirate."

"Ramón, come in now," his mother ordered. "Have your breakfast and tell me more about this bird."

But Ramón could not eat. He was too excited to sit still. He raced off into town and went straight to the *plaza*. Near the fountain, he saw his friend Miguel, who sold *piraguas*. Ramón tried to tell him about the red gull, but Miguel said, "Ramón, I have seen red fish, but there is no such thing as a red gull."

Ramón met his friend Alejandro, who sold newspapers. "The gull was red as fire, and could do as many tricks as my kite," he told him.

Alejandro laughed. "Ramón, if there was a red gull, his picture would be here in color on the front page of the newspaper."

Ramón walked to the other side of the *plaza*, where the island taxis were parked. There Carlos was painting some words on a window of his *público*, which he drove every day from Ponce to San Juan.

"It will say WHEELS OF FIRE," he told Ramón, as he stepped back to see if the letters were straight.

"Carlos, what would you say if I told you that I saw a sea gull this morning . . . a gull as red as the engine in the firehouse?"

"I would say that it was something that you saw in a dream," Carlos answered.

Ramón persisted. "It was laughing and stealing fish from a pelican."

Carlos put his brush down. "Ramón, if you go on with that story, you will make me spill this paint. My hand is shaking enough already."

Ramón sighed. How could he prove that he'd seen a red gull?

He stopped to look at the waves as he walked back home. The pelican was gone, and the beach was deserted. Then Ramón heard the sound again . . .

Haah . . . haah . . .

It came from the other side of some rocks that stood out in the water. Ramón scrambled over the slippery boulders. The gull was there, bright and red, fluttering among the rocks. It had a ruffled place on one of its wings and couldn't fly. "That pelican must have hurt you," Ramón said. He reached down and carefully picked up the gull. "I'll take you home, little pirate, and see if I can patch you up."

"That bird looks like a Christmas package," Señora Flora said, looking down into the box that Ramón was making into a comfortable nest. "He's a gull, but I have never seen a red gull before."

The bird stretched and combed its feathers. "If I let you go before you can fly, a big cat will get you," Ramón told him. "I will keep you until you are stronger."

Just then, he heard Alejandro calling, "Ramón, Ramón!" He was running toward the house, and Miguel and Carlos were following him. "Ramón, THE BIRD IS WANTED! There is a picture of it at the post office. If you have seen a red sea gull, you must report it to The Marine Research Station in San Juan!"

"He must be wanted for stealing fish," said Señora Flora.

"No," denied Miguel. "It could be a rare bird that is wanted for the zoo."

Ramón's mother looked worried. "You must take the gull to The Research Station in San Juan, Ramón. It is injured, and they will know what to do with it there."

"I will take you in my *público*," Carlos volunteered. "We can leave whenever you are ready."

Señora Flora's eyes sparkled, "I'll come with you. It's about time I visited my cousin in San Juan, anyhow."

A crowd gathered in the *plaza* to see Ramón leave with Señora Flora and Carlos. There were policemen, taxi drivers, shoppers, and storekeepers . . . even the Mayor had heard about the strange bird that was found in Ponce. They all cheered as Carlos drove off with a roar. Señora Flora waved, Ramón smiled, and the red gull flapped its wings.

Carlos drove along the coast to Salinas. They passed coconut groves and fields of waving sugar cane as he turned north. Then they started to climb the mountain. Carlos sounded his horn at every sharp curve and listened to hear if a car was coming from the opposite direction. At a bend in the road, Carlos stopped his *público* to pick up a passenger. He was a woodcarver who was taking a *cuatro* and a pair of carved fighting cocks to the market in San Juan.

"Buenos días," said Carlos. "We have urgent business in San Juan. My friend, Ramón, is taking this sea gull to The Research Station." Ramón showed the artist the gull in the box.

"Ahhh," the woodcarver exclaimed. "It is brighter than any of my painted birds."

In the valley, where a house on stilts leaned out over the hillside, Carlos stopped for another passenger, a girl. She was carrying a basket filled with flowers and big *yagruma* leaves.

"We are taking an important passenger to San Juan," Carlos announced. "Look, the bird is almost the color of your flowers." The sea gull stretched its wings and looked about the *público* with bright round eyes.

Carlos stopped his *público* again. A young man wearing a straw hat climbed in. He was carrying a sack full of masks made from dried coconut shells.

"What is that?" he asked when he saw the gull, "A bird dressed for the Carnival?"

Señora Flora told him the story of the injured gull.

In the distance, Ramón could see the north coast and the ocean gleaming just beyond it. The *público* passed through wooded hills that sloped down to the plains of the sugar *centrales*.

There was room for one more passenger, and at the edge of a cane field, Carlos stopped to pick up a boy. He was carrying a string of shiny green crabs.

"Push over. Make room for the boy," Señora Flora ordered. And to the boy she said, "You'd better hold those crabs out the window. We have a hungry sea gull here with a big appetite."

Carlos drove along the avenue that led to the heart of San Juan. As he passed the Plaza de Colón, he asked, "Señora Flora, shall I let you out here?"

"No," she replied quickly. "I'll go with Ramon. It is only a short walk from The Research Station to my cousin's house."

"I would like to come, too," the woodcarver said. "I have plenty of time."

"I think we should all go with Ramón," declared the boy with the string of crabs.

Carlos steered the *público* through the narrow streets of the city and parked at The Research Station. There, Ramón lifted the sea gull out of the box and carried it into the building. Señora Flora and

Carlos followed him; the other passengers were right behind them.

"You must want to see Señor Santiago," the lady at the desk said, when she saw the red bird in Ramón's arms. She led them to an office at the end of a hallway. "Señor Santiago," she said to a man seated at a desk. "Here is one of the gulls you are looking for."

"I found it on the beach in Ponce," Ramón reported. "He has hurt his wing."

"Well, that looks like one of our gulls." Señor Santiago smiled. "But we did not expect to have it delivered . . . like this."

"It is one of several gulls that we marked with a red dye to help us trace their winter migration routes. This one has traveled all the way from Woods Hole in Massachusetts," he pointed to a big map on the wall, "to here." His finger stopped at Puerto Rico. "It has come very far. Why don't you put this red pin into the map next to the town of Ponce," he said, giving a pin to Ramón.

"You mean," Carlos inquired, "that he is not a thief who is wanted for stealing fish from pelicans?"

"Of course not," Señor Santiago replied. "This is a laughing gull. Taking fish from pelicans is just one of their habits. They are clever enough to let other birds fish for them. If you leave the gull with us, we will see that it is cared for. As for the red color, it will disappear when the gull sheds its old feathers and grows new ones."

"So the gull is part of an experiment," said the woodcarver, nodding his head.

"It is not a thief, after all," said Señora Flora, and smiled.

"The red color will be gone in a few months," said the Señorita with the flowers.

"That gull will be flying again soon . . . and stealing fish, too," added Ramón.

"We must be going now, Ramón," Carlos said. "We have a long trip back to Ponce."

They all said goodbye, and Ramón shook hands with Señor Santiago.

It had been a long exciting day for Ramón. As the *público* started to climb the mountain road, he curled up in the back seat and fell asleep. He did not ever remember arriving back at his house near the beach.

The next morning, when he awoke, there was a bright patch of sunlight on the wall of his room. He looked out the window toward the palm trees. The water glistened, and he felt a gentle breeze from the beach. Then he saw it again. Ramón rubbed his eyes. It was a bright red spot in the sky. But the gull . . . the red gull was in San Juan.

Then Ramón heard his friend, Alejandro, calling from the beach. "Come, Ramón. Come and see the new kite I have made."

Author

A native of Rhode Island, Robert Barry spent ten years living in San Juan, Puerto Rico, where he was part owner of an art business. He knows firsthand the background of Ramon's story. Among other books by Mr. Barry is *Mr. Willowby's Christmas Tree*, a funny story about a wealthy man and the animals who borrowed his tree.

Sea Shopping

by Bette Killion

Low tide
  and the beach becomes
The sea's department store
  of treasures:
Conch shells, cat's eyes,
  olives, and sundials,
Sea stars, sand dollars,
  and a host of
White-to-brown little ones —
All crowding the bargain counters.

What do we pay
  for these treasures?
That's the lovely part!
Just a smile and a wave
  to the swooping gulls,
A race on the sands
  with a sandpiper,
A shriek of joy when the tide
  catches us unaware —
The shells are free to enjoy.

What Makes
a Bird
a BIRD?

by May Garelick

In trees and in bushes, at the edge of a brook, in the ground, and in the air, birds are flying, singing, calling, bathing, nesting.

How do we know that a bird is a bird? What makes it a bird? Is it a bird because it flies?

A fly flies. So do butterflies, ladybugs, dragonflies, and bees. But these are not birds. They are insects. Many insects fly. Not as fast as birds, not as far as birds, but many insects fly.

And what is this, flying around in the middle of the night?

It's not an insect. It's not a bird. It's a bat. All day bats hang upside down, asleep in hollow trees or in caves. At night they fly, catching insects to eat as they fly around.

Bats fly, insects fly, birds fly, and other things fly, too.

What do you think this is, flying above the water?

Is it a bat? An insect? A bird? No, it's a flying fish that has been frightened by an enemy under water. Like all fish, a flying fish lives most of the time in water. But if an enemy comes near, it can jump up out of the water, dart through the air, and escape.

Flying fish don't fly high and they don't fly far, but they fly higher and farther than some *birds*.

If there are flying insects, flying bats, and even flying fish, then it's not flying that makes a bird a bird. As a matter of fact, you know a *bird* that doesn't fly.

Have you ever seen a chicken fly? Hardly ever. Sometimes a chicken tries to fly. But it doesn't get far. To get anywhere a chicken walks.

Is a chicken a bird? Yes.

Another bird that doesn't fly is the ostrich. It's the biggest bird in the world, but it can't fly. An ostrich can run fast, though — even faster than a horse. No wonder. Look at those long legs. That's why the ostrich is such a fast runner.

Can you think of another bird that can't fly?

A penguin can't fly. Penguins walk. Down to the water they waddle, and into the sea for a swim.

If the ostrich can't fly, and penguins and chickens can't fly, what makes them birds? Are they birds because they have wings?

Birds have wings, all right. But look at a fly flying around. You can see its wings. And dragonflies and butterflies and bees have wings, too. Not all insects have wings, but those that fly have to have wings. Anything that flies has to have wings.

Then what about a chicken and an ostrich? They have wings but do not fly. Why? Their wings are too small to lift their bodies up in the air. The penguin's little wings are like flippers. They're fine for swimming but too small to lift the penguin up into the air. Still an ostrich, a chicken, and a penguin are birds. So it isn't wings that make a bird a bird.

Is a bird a thing that sings?

Birds sing and call to each other, especially in the spring. Some birds sing, some birds call, some cluck, some quack. That's how birds talk to each other.

One bird's song may mean, "This is my tree. Keep away." Usually other birds do keep away. If they don't, there's a fight.

"Chiree, chiree," a bird sings to a lady bird. Maybe his song means, "Come join me."

A mother hen clucks to her chicks to tell them food is here. "Cluck, cluck." And her baby chicks come running.

A duck quacks to her ducklings. "Quack, quack." And her ducklings follow her.

"Peep, peep," call the baby robins. And their parents know that the babies are hungry.

Birds sing and call messages to each other. But singing and calling is not what makes a bird a bird. Lots of *insects* sing and call their messages to each other, too.

Crickets chirp, and grasshoppers hum. Katydids repeat their rhythmic song all night long. *Katydid,*

katydid, katy didn't. And of all the insects, the tree cricket's song at night is the most beautiful. But these singers and callers are not birds. So it isn't singing that makes a bird a bird.

Then what *is* the special thing that makes a bird a bird? Is it a bird if it builds a nest?

Birds build nests in trees, in bushes, under leaves, in barns. Sometimes they even build nests in mailboxes — wherever their eggs and their babies will be safe. Birds' eggs must be kept warm in order to hatch. The nest and the mother's body keep the eggs warm.

But some birds build no nests at all. A whippoorwill lays her eggs on the ground. But the eggs are the color of the ground around them — camouflaged — so they are safe.

The penguin that lives in the cold, cold, icy Antarctic builds no nest. The mother lays one egg. Then the father penguin carries the egg on top of his feet, close to his body. That's how he keeps the egg warm for two months, until it is ready to hatch.

Is this a bird's nest? It looks like one, doesn't it? But it isn't. It's a hornet's nest.

Other creatures make nests. Ants and bees, snakes and fish, and rabbits and mice make nests.

Nest building is not the special thing that makes a bird a bird. Neither is egglaying. All birds lay eggs, it's true. But so do frogs, snakes, fish, bees, mosquitoes, and many other creatures.

So —

It's not flying that makes a bird different from anything else alive.

And it's not having wings.

And it's not singing or calling.

And it's not building nests or laying eggs.

What is it, then, that makes a bird a bird?

Birds have something that no other living thing has. What is it?

FEATHERS!

Only birds have feathers. That's the special thing that makes a bird a bird. A bird has to have feathers to be a bird. If it flies or not, if it sings or not; anything with feathers is a bird.

Feathers are strong. Try to break or tear one, and you'll see how strong a feather is. Bend a feather so the tip touches the bottom. Watch it spring back. It won't break.

Feathers are light. Hold a feather and you'll see how light it is. You've heard people say that something is "light as a feather."

Feathers are beautiful. They come in all colors. There are red cardinals, blue blue jays, black blackbirds, white doves, green parrots, brown sparrows, and many other colored birds in other colored feathers.

Feathers are useful, too. They do many things for birds. Their flight feathers make birds the best flyers. Even though other creatures fly, no living creature can fly as long or as far as a bird.

A bird has several layers of feathers. There's a cloak of feathers that helps keep birds warm in winter. Watch a bird on a cold day. It looks like a fat puffball because it has fluffed out its feathers to keep out the cold.

A layer of flat feathers helps keep birds cool in summer. The heat from the bird's body works its way out through these feathers.

Feathers help keep birds dry in the rain. Put a drop of water on a feather, and watch the water slide off.

Birds take good care of their feathers. Some birds bathe in water — ducking, splashing, spreading their wings. Some birds bathe in fine dust. After bathing, they preen their feathers carefully with their beaks. From an oil sac at the tail, birds take oil into their beaks to soften and straighten their feathers.

But no matter how well birds clean their feathers, they get brittle and wear out. About once a year birds molt — their worn out feathers fall out. Not all at once, just one or two at a time. And as they fall out, new feathers grow in.

You may find some of these old feathers on the ground. Pick them up and look at them.

Feathers are the special things that *make a bird a bird*.

Author

Russian-born May Garelick has worked in many different publishing jobs. She has written a number of children's books. Most are about nature or science, and several are about birds.

THE CAT'S PURR
Ashley Bryan

THE FIRE BRINGER
Margaret Hodges

WHY FROG AND SNAKE NEVER PLAY TOGETHER
Ashley Bryan

Houghton Mifflin Literature

Animal stories like the ones you've been reading make you wonder why. Have you ever wondered why cats purr . . . or why frogs and snakes don't play together? In the *Pourquoi Tales* (Why Stories) you will read imaginative answers to those and other questions. The authors are: Ashley Bryan, Margaret Hodges, Peter Parnall, David McCord, and John Ciardi.

Special
Friends

Through Grandpa's Eyes

by Patricia MacLachlan

Illustrated by Deborah Rey

Of all the houses that I know, I like my grandpa's best. My friend Peter has a new glass house with pebble-path gardens that go nowhere. And Maggie lives next door in an old wooden house with rooms behind rooms, all with carved doors and brass doorknobs. They are fine houses. But Grandpa's house is my favorite. Because I see it through Grandpa's eyes.

Grandpa is blind. He doesn't see the house the way I do. He has his own way of seeing.

In the morning, the sun pushes through the curtains into my eyes. I burrow down into the covers to get away, but the light follows me. I give up, throw back the covers, and run to Grandpa's room.

The sun wakes Grandpa differently from the way it wakes me. He says it touches him, *warming* him awake. When I peek around the door, Grandpa is already up and doing his morning exercises. Bending and stretching by the bed. He stops and smiles because he hears me.

"Good morning, John."

"Where's Nana?" I ask him.

"Don't you know?" he says, bending and stretching. "Close your eyes, John, and look through my eyes."

I close my eyes. Down below, I hear the banging of the pots and the sound of water running that I didn't hear before.

"Nana is in the kitchen, making breakfast," I say.

When I open my eyes again, I can see Grandpa nodding at me. He is tall with dark gray hair.

And his eyes are sharp blue even though they are not sharp seeing.

I exercise with Grandpa. Up and down. Then I try to exercise with my eyes closed.

"One, two," says Grandpa, "three, four."

"Wait!" I cry. I am still on one, two when Grandpa is on three, four.

I fall sideways. Three times. Grandpa laughs as he hears my thumps on the carpet.

"Breakfast!" calls Nana from downstairs.

"I smell eggs frying," says Grandpa. He bends his head close to mine. "And buttered toast."

The wooden banister on the stairway has been worn smooth from Grandpa running his fingers up and down. I walk behind him, my fingers following Grandpa's smooth path.

We go into the kitchen.

"I smell flowers," says Grandpa.

"What flowers?" I ask.

He smiles. He loves guessing games.

"Not violets, John, not peonies . . ."

"Carnations!" I cry. *I* love guessing games.

"Silly." Grandpa laughs. "Marigolds. Right, Nana?"

Nana laughs, too.

"That's too easy," she says, putting two plates of food in front of us.

"It's not too easy," I protest. "How can Grandpa tell? All the smells mix together in the air."

"Close your eyes, John," says Nana. "Tell me what breakfast is."

"I smell the eggs. I smell the toast," I say, my eyes closed. "And something else. The something else doesn't smell good."

"*That* something else," says Nana, smiling, "is the marigolds."

When he eats, Grandpa's plate of food is a clock.

"Two eggs at nine o'clock and toast at two o'clock," says Nana to Grandpa. "And a dollop of jam."

"A dollop of jam," I tell Grandpa, "at six o'clock."

I make my plate of food a clock, too, and eat through Grandpa's eyes.

After breakfast, I follow Grandpa's path through the dining room to the living room, to the window that he opens to feel the weather outside, to the table where he finds his pipe, and to his cello in the corner.

"Will you play with me, John?" he asks.

He tunes our cellos without looking. I play with a music stand and music before me. I know all about sharps and flats. I see them on the music. But Grandpa plays them. They are in his fingers. For a moment I close my eyes and play through Grandpa's eyes. My fingering hand slides up and down the cello neck — toward the pegs for flats, toward the bridge for sharps. But with my eyes closed my bow falls from the strings.

"Listen," says Grandpa. "I'll play a piece I learned when I was your age. It was my favorite."

He plays the tune while I listen. That is the way Grandpa learns new pieces. By listening.

"Now," says Grandpa. "Let's do it together."

"That's fine," says Grandpa as we play. "But C sharp, John," he calls to me. "C sharp!"

Later, Nana brings out her clay to sculpt my Grandpa's head.

"Sit still," she grumbles.

"I won't," he says, imitating her grumbly voice, making us laugh.

While she works, Grandpa takes out his piece of wood. He holds it when he's thinking. His fingers move back and forth across the wood, making smooth paths like the ones on the stair banister.

"Can I have a piece of thinking wood, too?" I ask.

Grandpa reaches in his shirt pocket and tosses a small bit of wood in my direction. I catch it. It is smooth with no splinters.

"The river is up," says Nana.

Grandpa nods a short nod. "It rained again last night. Did you hear the gurgling in the rain gutter?"

As they talk, my fingers begin a river on my thinking wood. The wood will winter in my pocket so when I am not át Grandpa's house I can still think about Nana, Grandpa, and the river.

When Nana is finished working, Grandpa runs his hand over the sculpture, his fingers soft and quick like butterflies.

"It looks like me," he says, surprised.

My eyes have already told me that it looks like Grandpa. But he shows me how to feel his face with my three middle fingers, and then the clay face.

"Pretend your fingers are water," he tells me.

My waterfall fingers flow down his clay head, filling in the spaces beneath the eyes like little pools before they flow down over the cheeks. It does feel like Grandpa. This time my fingers tell me.

Grandpa and I walk outside, through the front yard and across the field to the river. Grandpa has not been blind forever. He remembers in his mind the gleam of the sun on the river, the Queen Anne's lace in the meadow, and every dahlia in his garden. But he gently takes my elbow as we walk so that I can help show him the path.

"I feel a south wind," says Grandpa.

I can tell which way the wind is blowing because I see the way the tops of the trees lean. Grandpa tells by the feel of the meadow grasses and by the way his hair blows against his face.

When we come to the riverbank, I see that Nana was right. The water is high and has cut in by the

willow tree. It flows around and among the roots of the tree, making paths. Paths like Grandpa's on the stair banister and on the thinking wood. I see a blackbird with a red patch on its wing sitting on a cattail. Without thinking, I point my finger.

"What is that bird, Grandpa?" I ask excitedly.

"*Conk-a-ree,*" the bird calls to us.

"A red-winged blackbird," says Grandpa promptly.

He can't see my finger pointing. But he hears the song of the bird.

"And somewhere behind the blackbird," he says, listening, "a song sparrow."

I hear a scratchy song, and I look and look until I see the earth-colored bird that Grandpa knows is here.

Nana calls from the front porch of the house.

"Nana's made hot bread for lunch," he tells me happily. "And spice tea." Spice tea is his favorite.

I close my eyes, but all I can smell is the wet earth by the river.

As we walk back to the house, Grandpa stops suddenly. He bends his head to one side, listening. He points his finger upward.

"Honkers," he whispers.

I look up and see a flock of geese, high in the clouds, flying in a V.

"Canada geese," I tell him.

"Honkers," he insists. And we both laugh.

We walk up the path again and to the yard where Nana is painting the porch chairs. Grandpa smells the paint.

"What color, Nana?" he asks. "I cannot smell the color."

"Blue," I tell him, smiling. "Blue like the sky."

"Blue like the color of Grandpa's eyes," Nana says.

When he was younger, before I can remember, before he was blind, Grandpa did things the way I do. Now, when we drink tea and eat lunch on the porch, Grandpa pours his own cup of tea by putting his finger just inside the rim of the cup to tell him when it is full. He never burns his finger. Afterward, when I wash the dishes, he feels them as he dries them. He even sends some back for me to wash again.

"Next time," says Grandpa, pretending to be cross, "I wash, you dry."

In the afternoon, Grandpa, Nana, and I take our books outside to read under the apple tree. Grandpa reads his book with his fingers, feeling the raised Braille dots that tell him the words.

As he reads, Grandpa laughs out loud.

"Tell us what's funny," says Nana. "Read to us, Papa."

And he does.

Nana and I put down our books to listen. A gray squirrel comes down the trunk of the apple tree, tail high, and seems to listen, too. But Grandpa doesn't see him.

After supper, Grandpa turns on the television. I watch, but Grandpa listens, and the music and the words tell him when something is dangerous or funny, happy or sad.

Somehow, Grandpa knows when it is dark, and he takes me upstairs and tucks me into bed. He bends down to kiss me, his hands feeling my head.

"You need a haircut, John," he says.

Before Grandpa leaves, he pulls the light chain above my bed to turn out the light. But, by mistake, he's turned it on instead. I lie for a moment after he's gone, smiling, before I get up to turn off the light.

Then, when it is dark for me the way it is dark for Grandpa, I hear the night noises that Grandpa hears. The house creaking, the birds singing their last songs of the day, the wind rustling the tree outside my window.

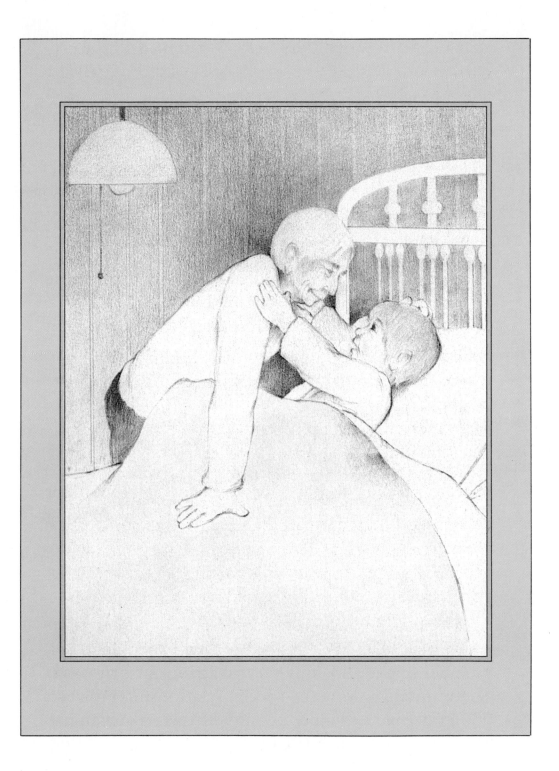

Then, all of a sudden, I hear the sounds of geese overhead. They fly low over the house.

"Grandpa," I call softly, hoping he's heard them too.

"Honkers," he calls back.

"Go to sleep, John," says Nana.

Grandpa says her voice smiles to him. I test it.

"What?" I call to her.

"I said go to sleep," she answers.

She says it sternly. But Grandpa is right. Her voice smiles to me. I know. Because I'm looking through Grandpa's eyes.

Author

Through Grandpa's Eyes is the second book written by Patricia MacLachlan. She used her experiences as a member of a local family service agency in writing it. She wanted to show the special relationship between young people and older people. Ms. MacLachlan has also been an English teacher.

What's the Matter with Carruthers?

**Written and illustrated
by James Marshall**

One fall morning Emily Pig and her friend Eugene were taking a stroll in the park.

"What beautiful weather," said Emily. "I'm sure we are going to meet some of our friends here today."

"That would be very nice indeed," said Eugene. "It's such fun to bump into friends and have a little chat."

And sure enough, just around the bend, they came upon their old friend Carruthers, all bundled up in his muffler and sitting alone on a wooden bench. He was gazing at the falling leaves.

"Good morning, Carruthers," they called out in their most cheerful voices.

"Good morning," said Carruthers. But his voice was far from cheerful. It was the kind of "good morning," that really means, "Don't bother me. I want to be left alone."

"I'm worried about Carruthers," whispered Emily to Eugene. "He hasn't been himself lately. He's so grumpy and unpleasant."

"It's not like Carruthers to be unpleasant," Eugene whispered back. "He always has a kind word for everyone."

"Yesterday," said Emily, "I saw him do such a disgraceful thing. You may find this hard to believe, but Carruthers actually stuck out his tongue at someone!"

Eugene was shocked. "It's not like Carruthers to be rude. He has always had such lovely manners."

"But that's not all," said Emily. "The children in the park are complaining. It seems that Carruthers took away their ball."

"Oh, no!" exclaimed Eugene. "I just can't understand it. It is certainly not like Carruthers to be mean. He has always been so fond of children."

Leaving Carruthers to sit alone on his bench and gaze at the falling leaves, Emily and Eugene continued their stroll through the park.

"There must be something that we can do to lift Carruthers's spirits," said Emily. "And we had better do it soon. If Carruthers continues to act the way he has been acting, he won't have any friends left."

"That's very true," said Eugene. "No one likes a grouch."

And so the two friends sat together on a large rock and thought long and hard.

"Well," Eugene began, after a long pause, "whenever I'm in a grouchy and unpleasant mood, I always listen to beautiful music. In no time at all I feel much better, and I'm sure that I'm much more pleasant to be around."

"That gives me an idea," said Emily. "Come with me."

The two friends hurried home, but in a few minutes, they were back in the park with their musical instruments. Emily was carrying her tuba, and Eugene had his tambourine.

"What a good idea," said Eugene. "When we smooth Carruthers' rumpled nerves with our beautiful music, he'll be his old friendly self again. I'm sure that he'll be so grateful."

Turning the bend, they saw Carruthers, still sitting in the same place, still gazing at the falling leaves. And ever so quietly they tiptoed up behind him.

Placing the mouthpiece of her tuba to her lips, Emily puffed up her cheeks and began to play, softly

at first and then quite loudly. Eugene tapped on his tambourine.

"Um-Pah Um-Pah Tap Tap. Um-Pah Um-Pah Tap Tap." It sounded something like that.

But Carruthers was not impressed. Instead of listening to the music, he put his paws to his ears and growled, "That is the most awful noise I have ever heard in my life!"

And he promptly got up and walked away.

Emily Pig and Eugene looked at each other. "Maybe we should have practiced more," said Eugene.

"No," replied his friend, "some bears just don't and never will appreciate good music."

Emily set her tuba on the bench and sat down beside it. "But just because we could not improve Carruthers' mood with our music, that does not mean that we should give up. We must think of another way."

"Yes," replied Eugene, "we must not give up."

So once again they thought long and hard.

"Whenever I am in a grumpy mood," said Emily, "I always have a little snack. I'm sure that a tasty snack would be just the thing for Carruthers. Maybe he hasn't been getting enough to eat lately. Why don't we invite him to lunch for honey cakes and tea? You know how partial bears are to honey cakes."

"What a clever idea," said Eugene. "Let's go to your house right away and send Carruthers an invitation to come to lunch."

Carruthers was in an even grouchier mood when he came home from the park and found the invitation to lunch waiting for him. Certainly he was in no mood to go visiting — but what bear can resist honey cakes? So of course he went.

At Emily's house Carruthers was given the very best chair. Emily poured the tea and Eugene brought out the honey cakes.

"It's another beautiful day, isn't it?" said Emily, trying to start a friendly conversation.

"Not really," said Carruthers.

"You must enjoy strolling in the park," said Eugene.

"Not especially," said Carruthers.

"My, how lovely your fur looks today, Carruthers," said Emily.

"I've never cared for it," said Carruthers.

Emily and Eugene didn't know what else to say, Carruthers was so determined to be unpleasant. And so the tea party continued in silence, except for the sound of Carruthers munching on honey cakes and sipping tea.

When the cake plate and the teapot were both empty, Eugene tried again. "My goodness, Carruthers,

you certainly must like Emily's honey cakes. You've eaten all twelve dozen of them."

"They were very tasty," said Carruthers. "Thank you for inviting me, but I must leave now. Stuffy in here."

"Yes, it is stuffy," said Emily. "Why don't we all go for a walk in the fresh air?"

"I don't like walking," said Carruthers.

"Then why don't we all go for a drive?" said Eugene.

"A splendid idea!" exclaimed Emily. "I'm sure a change of scene will do wonders for Carruthers."

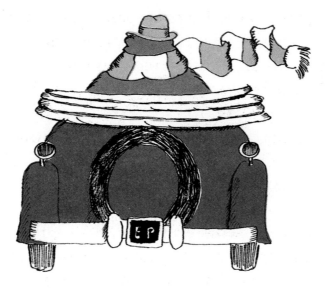

And before Carruthers could say anything at all, he found himself all bundled up again and sitting in the back seat of Emily's traveling car.

Very soon the three friends were sailing through the open countryside.

"There's nothing like a drive in the country to cheer the spirits," called out Eugene.

"The countryside gives me hay fever," was all Carruthers would say.

Not far down the road they passed a large sign.

"Ah," said Emily.

"Ah," said Eugene.

"Ugh," said Carruthers, "I hate amusement parks."

But Emily and Eugene paid no attention, no attention at all. "Rides and games are just what Carruthers needs," whispered Eugene.

"Yes," said Emily. "We are going, and that is that."

When they got to the park Carruthers asked to stay in the car, but Emily would have none of that. "Nonsense, Carruthers, you must not be a bad sport."

Carruthers had never been very good at arguing, especially with Emily, and so he went in to the amusement park. And he rode all the rides and played all the games that Emily told him to play.

But nothing seemed to improve his mood. He didn't smile even once. Not even on the ferris wheel, which had always been his favorite ride. He grumbled all through the fun house and looked distinctly annoyed in the tunnel of love. And even after Carruthers had won several lovely prizes, he was still the grouch he had been all day. "I think it's time to go home. I'm not having a good time."

Emily and Eugene were so discouraged, "I was sure this would work," said Emily. "It seems to me that we have tried just about everything, and Carruthers hasn't improved one little bit."

"Yes," said Eugene, "I suppose there is nothing to do but take Carruthers home."

On the way home no one spoke.

But when the roadster pulled in front of Carruthers' little house, Emily had one last idea. "Carruthers," she said, "just look at all those leaves in your front yard. What a messy housekeeper you are. I really think we should help you rake some of them up before evening."

Now this was an idea that Carruthers did not like at all. Raking leaves in the late afternoon was not exactly his notion of fun, but he knew that Emily was going to have her way again. And he went off to find three rakes and a bushel basket.

"I don't see why we should help Carruthers rake his leaves," said Eugene to Emily, "after all we have done for him today."

But Emily had made up her mind. "Sometimes keeping very busy is a good way to get out of a grumpy mood," she explained.

"We might as well give it a try," sighed Eugene.

When Carruthers returned, the three leaf-rakers set to work. Emily and Carruthers raked leaves into the bushel basket, and Eugene emptied the contents onto a pile he had started.

Very soon the pile was quite high.

"If we hurry," said Emily, "we will be finished in time for supper."

But Carruthers was already beginning to slow down.

He started to yawn. A small yawn, which he covered with his paw, to be polite. Then a much bigger yawn.

But then — a great big bear yawn.

And without a word of warning, Carruthers plopped headfirst into the huge pile of leaves.

"Oh my goodness!" cried Eugene. "What in the world has happened?"

The two friends quickly cleared away the pile of leaves and uncovered Carruthers.

"He's asleep!" they exclaimed.

"So that is why Carruthers has been such an awful grouch lately," said Emily. "Why didn't we think of this before? He forgot that it was time for his long winter's sleep."

"Of course," said Eugene. "Carruthers should have been tucked away in bed several days ago. No wonder he has been so impossible to be around."

"There is no use waking him now," said Emily. "He'll be asleep for the rest of the winter. It's up to us to get him into bed."

"That will be the hardest job yet," said Eugene.

But after a lot of huffing and puffing they managed to lift the sleeping Carruthers, who was just beginning to snore, into a small wagon and pull it into the house.

When they got to Carruthers's bedroom, they huffed and puffed again and ever so slowly put Carruthers under the heavy winter covers. Emily pulled his nightcap snugly down around his ears. Eugene set the alarm clock for spring and drew the shades.

"Good night, Carruthers," whispered Emily, giving him a kiss on the cheek. "Sleep tight, and we'll see you in the spring when you will be your old sweet self again."

Author

James Marshall is well known as a writer and illustrator of animal stories. His first book, *George and Martha,* became so popular that he wrote several more books about the two hippos. Friendship is a favorite theme in Mr. Marshall's writing. Emily and Eugene, the friends you just read about, appear again in *Yummers!* and in *Taking Care of Carruthers.*

Furry Bear

by A. A. Milne

If I were a bear,
   And a big bear too,
I shouldn't much care
   If it froze or snew;
I shouldn't much mind
   If it snowed or friz —
I'd be all fur-lined
   With a coat like his!
For I'd have fur boots and a brown fur wrap,
And brown fur knickers and a big fur cap.
I'd have a fur muffle-ruff to cover my jaws,
And brown fur mittens on my big brown paws,
With a big brown furry-down up to my head,
I'd sleep all the winter in a big fur bed.

Brave Janet Reachfar

by Jane Duncan

Illustrated by Cherie Wyman

Everybody called Janet "Janet Reachfar" because the farm which was her home was named "Reachfar". It lay on top of a hill in the Highlands of Scotland and looked down towards the sea.

The nearest house to Reachfar was two miles away but Janet never felt lonely. She had her dog called Fly and her ferret called Angus. She also had her family: her grandfather and grandmother, her father and mother, her aunt and her special friends, Tom and George, who did most of the work about the farm.

Janet's grandfather was very old, with a long white beard, and he was a little deaf. He spoke very seldom and went about the farm by himself. Janet saw her father only in the evenings, for he managed another farm all day. Her grandmother, her mother and Aunt Kate were usually too busy to talk to Janet very much — especially her grandmother who, Janet thought, must be the busiest woman in the whole world.

Granny was always bustling about and "laying down the law" or being "on about" things, as George and Tom called it. Only they did not call her "Granny" when she was on about things — they called her "Herself".

One noonday in spring, when Janet and her family were sitting at the big kitchen table having their dinner, the sun suddenly seemed to disappear and the sky went dark. Big flakes of snow began to fly past the window.

"I *told* you this was coming," Granny, said, and it was in her "Herself" voice.

Granny always seemed to know when it was going to rain and when there was going to be a gale. George and Tom said that there was a little man who lived in the brown jug on the top shelf of the dresser who told Granny about the weather, but Janet knew that this was not true. One day when everybody was out of the house, Janet had climbed right up and looked inside the jug and there was nothing in it but a few nails and a dead spider.

"I told you," Herself said again, "but none of you ever listens to *me. You* know best all the time."

This was not true either. Janet thought that everybody at Reachfar was always listening to Herself all the time. You could not help it.

"I said it was too early in the year to put the sheep out on the High Moor and the East Hill," Herself went on. "So don't blame me now that you have to go and bring them all back into the shelter of the Home Wood again."

She spoke as if everybody was arguing with her but nobody was saying a word. Everybody was watching the snow, which was growing thicker and thicker and piling up on the frames of the windowpanes.

"*If Candelmas be bright and fair, half the winter's to come and more,*" Herself said. "And Candlemas this year was like a day in June. So finish your dinner, George and Tom, and fetch the sheep back into the wood."

"Yes, Mistress," Tom and George said together.

They put on their heavy coats and mufflers, took their tall sticks, from the rack in the passage, and called their sheepdogs, Moss and Fan, out of the barn. Then they set off towards the gate that led to the High Moor. Janet followed them with Fly, but she did not go further than the gate. The High Moor was a forbidden place.

"We will gather the big flock off the Heights first, Tom," George said at the gate. "Those thirty ewes on the East Hill will have to wait til we get back. Run along into the house, Janet, out of all this snow and cold."

Janet and Fly turned back down the farmyard, but they did not go into the house. There was no point, with Herself on about nobody ever listening to her.

Janet went into the stable and climbed up to sit on the edge of Betsy's manger, while Fly lay down on a sack by the wall.

Stroking Betsy's face, Janet thought about her grandmother. She was a magic sort of person — something like a witch, but not an ugly or wicked witch. She was rather beautiful, really. Her "on abouts" did not last very long, and soon she would turn back into the person they called Granny, who was gentle and wise.

Almost magically wise. Granny always seemed to know where you had been and what you had been up to, even when you were far away and out of her sight. It seemed to Janet that Granny knew not only about the weather, but about every single thing in the whole world.

Janet gave Betsy's neck a final pat and climbed down from the manger, saying inside her head the rhyme that she, Tom and George had made:

When Herself is on-about
The three of us are better out.

Herself would have changed back into Granny by tea-time, but meanwhile Janet decided to go to the barn to have a chat with Angus, her ferret.

Angus, however, made it quite clear that he did not want to be chatted to. When Janet spoke to him, he opened his pink eyes for a moment, shut them again, snuffled, and curled himself up more tightly. Janet shut his box and went through the door at the end of the barn into the byre.

Maggie, the big black cow, was lying on her side in her stall among the warm straw. She was more welcoming. She gave her head a shake and her tail a twitch, inviting Janet and Fly to sit down and lean against her fat warm body. Then she went on chewing her cud, her big tongue flicking round and round inside her mouth.

Feeling the warmth of Maggie, Janet began to think of the poor sheep out on the cold East Hill. She could not stop thinking about them. It would take George and Tom a long time to bring down the flock from the High Moor. The ewes on the East Hill would have a very long wait . . . .

Suddenly Janet stood up. She buttoned up her coat and put on her woollen hood and gloves. "Heel, Fly," she said as they left the warm steamy byre for the snow and cold of out-of-doors.

The East Hill was a long way off, and today it seemed longer than ever. The wind kept trying to blow Janet and Fly backwards as they plodded through the deepening snow on the path through the wood. At last, though, they came to the little gate that led out of the corner of the wood onto the bare hill where the snow was like a thick cloud of feathers.

When Janet took off her glove to undo the latch on the gate, her fingers went stiff with the cold. The East Hill was a forbidden place, too, but Janet did not intend to go right out on to it, not *right* out *on* to it.

"Seek, Fly!" she said, waving her arm at the hill just like Tom or George. "Sheep! Go seek!"

The dog crouched low, so that her dark furry body seemed to slide under the blowing snow. She ran out onto the hill, while Janet waited in the shelter of the trees by the gate.

Soon the sheep began to come towards Janet, "One, two, three — " she counted as the woolly creatures galloped one by one through the narrow gateway, baa-ing as if to say thank you for the shelter of the trees.

"Twenty-nine," Janet said when Fly came to look up at her. "One more, Fly! Go seek!"

Fly disappeared into the snow again and was gone for a long time. When she came back she brought no sheep with her. She put her paws up to Janet's chest and then began to dance round and round, barking all the time and making bigger and bigger circles that took her further and further out on the hill.

She wanted Janet to follow her but Janet was not sure about this. Besides being forbidden, the East Hill under the blowing snow was very wild, bare and frightening. In the end, though, she decided to trust Fly who always knew the way home. She shut the little gate and stepped out into the deep snow and driving wind.

She was completely out of breath and her legs felt as if they were going to break with tiredness when, at last, Fly nuzzled into a hummock of snow and exposed the head of a sheep.

"Baa-aa," the sheep said in a weak tired voice as Janet and Fly began to dig the snow away. Fly dug very quickly with her forepaws, making the snow fly up in cloud behind her. But it was Janet who found the baby lamb, quite newly born and tucked in close to its mother.

"Stop, Fly," Janet said, for she knew that if she picked up the lamb and began to walk away, the mother sheep would struggle free and follow her.

Janet unbuttoned her coat, put the lamb inside, and fastened the coat again with the lamb's head sticking out between the two top buttons. When Janet and Fly started to walk away, the mother sheep began to struggle hard, baa-ing pitifully. It seemed she could not get up.

"Dig, Fly!" Janet said, and soon they found that a piece of the wire fence was wound round and round the sheep's leg. Her struggling was only pulling it tighter, so that it was cutting the leg painfully.

Janet's hands were not strong enough to bend the wire, though she tried for some time. At last she sat down in the snow, her chin resting on the lamb's head which stuck out on her chest. Fly sat down too, her head on one side, her golden eyes looking from the sheep to Janet as if to say, "What do we do now?"

This was the first time, Janet thought, that Fly had ever asked her this question. Until now Fly had always known best what to do. Fly knew that the stackyard ladder was too high to climb and took Janet's skirt in her sharp teeth and pulled her down. Fly knew that the ice on the duckpond was not thick enough to walk on and pulled Janet back. But now it was up to Janet.

She thought hard. Then she took off her woollen hood and untied her blue hair-ribbon. Her fingers were numb as she tied the ribbon tightly on Fly's collar. Her lips were stiff with cold, too, as she said, "George and Tom, Fly! George and Tom!"

Fly did not want to go. She turned her head to sniff at the ends of the ribbon, then looked back at Janet.

"Fetch George, Tom!" Janet repeated sternly, pointing across the hill to where she thought the wood and home were. She could not be sure. The flying snow made the air so blackly dark that it seemed to shut all the world away.

Suddenly Fly made up her mind. With the wind behind her now, she dashed away, the ends of blue ribbon streaming from her collar.

Janet tucked herself close into the woolly side of the sheep, took off her wet gloves, and put her cold hands inside her coat to cuddle the lamb. She tried not to feel frightened.

The snow piled up around them, while the wind howled and shrieked across the hill. Janet began to feel warm, cosy, and sleepy, as if the world and the storm were going further and further away. She did not know that this deceiving warm sleepiness some-times causes people to snuggle down and be found long afterwards, frozen to death.

87

She was quite startled when she heard barking close beside her. Fly began to dig, her blue ribbon still streaming in the wind, and then Moss and Fan were there and began to dig too.

"Out of it! Get back, dogs!" said George's voice, and Janet found herself being lifted, shivering now, out of the snowy hole that had been so cosy and warm. George turned her over his arm and began to pat her quite hard on the back. The shivering stopped.

"Careful!" she said, coming wide awake. "Mind my lamb, you clumsy, big lump!"

"Merciful goodness," Tom said. "She has a lamb!"

"The mother sheep is hurt," Janet told them. "She has got wire —"

"We'll soon see to that," Tom said, and with his strong fingers he began to untwist the wire that Janet had not been able to bend.

Janet was safe now from the storm, standing beside George and Tom, who always made everything safe. But she began to feel another kind of fear. She suddenly remembered that she was forbidden to come out onto the East Hill like this, and that there would be a scolding from Herself when she got home.

With the lamb's head still under her chin, Janet looked up at George. "Herself and Mother are going to be angry," she said.

"Angry? After you bringing in the flock from the Hill and bringing home the first lamb of the spring?" George asked. "Have you gone foolish in your head?"

89

The mother sheep gave a loud "Baa!" and sprang to her feet. She was limping a little, but she would soon be all right. She came close to Janet to sniff at her lamb's head.

"About the East Hill, here," Janet said. "Herself will be very angry."

"*What* East Hill?" George asked, looking around as if he had never heard of the East Hill. "Speaking for myself, I cannot see anything through all this snow. I do not see any East Hill around here."

"Nor me, either, forbye," Tom said. "And besides, it is my opinion that we are no further from home than the fence round the wood. And I will tell you something more. We are going to be late for tea, and Herself will be so angry about that, likely she will have no angriness left for anything else. Come on!"

They all began to walk with the snow blowing behind them. Janet had no idea of the way home, but that did not matter, for not only was Fly there but George and Tom as well.

As they walked, they began to make a rhyme, and by the time they reached the gate into the farmyard it was finished. They told it to Herself as soon as they went into the house:

> *Janet found the first-born lamb*
> *Near the East Hill gate.*
> *Its mother's leg was stuck in some wire*
> *And that is why we are late.*

Herself looked from Tom to George, and then on to Janet with the lamb's head under her chin. This was her suspecting look — the look she wore when she suspected that Janet, George, and Tom had been up to something.

"Baa!" the little lamb said in a small voice.

"That is enough of your silly rhymes and nonsense," Herself said sternly. "George, take the lamb out to the fold to its mother where it belongs."

"Right away, Granny," George said, beginning to undo Janet's coat.

"This very minute, Granny," Tom said.

Now Janet knew that everything was all right. But she also knew that on their way to the fold with the lamb, George and Tom would be calling Granny "Herself," for she was still laying down the law.

"And you take those wet things off," she was saying to Janet, "and sit down at the table beside *your* mother where *you* belong."

Janet did as she was told, and Herself went on, "Sometimes I think the people of Reachfar have no sense at all, putting sheep out, taking them in, and prowling about among the snow and the cold as if they had no brains in their heads. It is a wonder that some of *them* don't get lost in the snow."

Janet's mother was very quiet and spoke always in a soft voice. She spoke now. "If they got lost in the snow, Granny, you would have nobody to scold. That would be terrible, wouldn't it?" she said.

Herself looked at Mother, and Janet watched her change back into Granny. Mother could always make her do this.

Granny smiled at Janet. "But you are a clever girl, finding the first lamb of the spring like that," she said. "Eat a big tea. You must be very hungry after going such a long, *long* way, all by yourself, to find that lamb."

Granny took the lid off the big black pot on the fire and stirred the supper soup. With the firelight shining on her face and white hair, she did look like a witch — a wise, kind sort of witch who knew by magic that you had gone to a forbidden place, but that you had done it for a good reason and must be forgiven.

Janet Reachfar ate a boiled egg, a scone with butter, two scones with raspberry jam and a piece of shortbread. It was a very satisfactory tea.

Author

Jane Duncan, a Scottish author of many books for adults and children, had a family home in the far northern highlands of Scotland. It is the setting for the story you have just read. Janet's adventures continue in *Janet Reachfar and the Kelpie* and *Janet Reachfar and the Chickabird,* which were written just before the author's death in 1976.

More Stories Julian Tells

by Ann Cameron
Illustrated by Ann Strugnell

❧ *Houghton Mifflin Literature* ❧

You've been reading about several special friend-ships. When you read *More Stories Julian Tells* by Ann Cameron, you will think about your own growing-up adventures. Julian tells stories about his relationships with his brother, his best friend, and his father.

3

Hopes and Dreams

The Skates
of Uncle Richard

Excerpts from the book
by Carol Fenner
Illustrated by Vincent Morgan

Once there was an ice-skating champion, a beautiful black figure skater.

She was tall and smooth and slender. She could swoop across the ice and leap into a double turn high in the middle of the air. She could spin so fast she could hardly be seen except for a whirling blur. She could also do a flying camel — a beautiful, slow spin on one leg, her body bent sideways into her reaching arms.

Her hair was braided into tight little ropes across her head, showing its fine shape. She had brown eyes that shone in a round, brown face. Her picture was in the paper on the sports page. Television cameras followed her around while she skated so that people could watch her in their living rooms.

But there was only one person who knew where she lived. A girl named Marsha knew — because the beautiful black figure skater lived inside Marsha's head.

The big, gleaming skating arena lived in Marsha's head, too. And the music that was played. And the audience in the shadowy stands. And the television cameras.

Marsha was almost nine years old. She dreamed of discovering lost heroes and helping them home. She dreamed of mystery and finding clues and solving crimes. But, most of all, she dreamed of being a figure skater . . . tall and smooth and slender and able to spin and fly across the ice.

The ice skates of her dreams were snow-white with gleaming blades. They had red pompons, and little bells on the laces. On the front of the blades were little saw-toothed points, like little teeth. Marsha didn't know what the teeth were for, but she knew that they were important to a figure skater.

Marsha herself had never skated with real ice skates on real ice. Sometimes she skated without skates. She would stand alone in her room, her arms lifted in the empty air. She would bend forward and extend one leg behind. She could even imagine the coolness drifting up from the ice. But that was not nearly as satisfying as being the champion star skater who lived in her head.

Her older brother Leonard had ice skates with long, straight racing blades. He had mowed lawns one summer and bought them with the money he earned. Last winter, on one of his good-mood days, he had taken Marsha with him to the lagoon where everyone skated. Marsha had run and skidded about in her snow boots. But her legs had felt leaden and her heart couldn't soar. She felt miles away from being the beautiful skater of her dreams.

Summer came with all the long, warm days. Marsha turned nine. She learned how to swim. She rode on swings in the park. She helped her mother weed the garden. She played detective with her best friend. But Marsha's dream followed her into summer. At night, while the warm air drifted through her open window, she dreamed of ice skating.

When the leaves began to change color, she grew excited at the thought of colder days and the lagoon freezing over. The dream followed her to school, and her mind would be far away when she was supposed to be thinking about numbers or the way words go together.

The days grew shorter and shorter. Then one day it snowed. Winter was really on its way. Thoughts of Christmas came into Marsha's dreaming head. She began to hint to her mother that she sure would like ice skates for Christmas this year.

Marsha didn't think she would ever get ice skates for Christmas. Her mother always seemed to get her things she thought Marsha should have, not things Marsha really wanted. One of her mother's favorite expressions was, "Money spent wisely lasts forever."

Marsha worried a little, too, about what would happen to the beautiful skater in her head if the real Marsha ever got real ice skates on her real feet. Her dream skating, her leaps and spins, might not come true at all. Still she kept on hinting.

Gradually, whenever Marsha brought up the subject of ice skates, her mother would look sort of thoughtful. Marsha's hopes rose. But her worry about losing the dream skater who lived in her head rose, too.

Christmas Day came closer. Marsha thought about ice skates with a terrible excitement and a little bit of dread.

Leonard, who had crept about trying to locate hidden presents, began to wear a knowing smirk on his face. Marsha wondered if he'd seen her ice skates hidden somewhere. She didn't ask because she was afraid to know.

On Christmas morning, Marsha's eyes flew over the piles of packages to a large box covered with red tissue. It had silver stars pasted into the shape of her initial, a big starry "M." Her heart crowded into her throat.

She couldn't bring herself to open the red box right away. First she opened a flat box with a red-striped, homemade apron in it. She unwrapped a new plaid dress with a lace collar. There were two new books for her. But her mind was on the box covered with red tissue. She grew first hot, then cold, from excitement.

Finally the present covered with red tissue was the only one left to open. Marsha tore at the tissue, careful not to rip into the big "M." When she opened the box up, there inside the whispering tissue were the ugliest ice skates she had ever seen.

For a while, Marsha just sat staring at the skates. Then dumbly she took them out of the box. They were old-fashioned hockey skates, black with brown leather around the thick toes and brown circles at the ankles. They had heavy, blunted blades, meant for charging, meant for stopping short and turning hard. They were not in the least the kind of skates for doing the flying camel or executing a perfect figure eight. And, although the blades were clean and shining, the skates had obviously been used and used and used before.

"They were your Uncle Richard's," said her mother. "They were his skates when he was seven. He was about your size then. He kept them up real nice. They're almost good as new."

Marsha kept her eyes on the skates. Uncle Richard was old now . . . old, at least thirty. She could feel tears pushing to get out behind her eyes.

"Your Uncle Richard is a fine skater," her mother continued. "He learned how to skate on those skates. They'll be a good start for you, Marsha, till we see how you take to skating."

Marsha sat on the floor with the box at her side, the ugly skates in her lap. "I remembered packing them away in the attic years ago," her mother was saying. "Richard'll be pleased to know they're being used."

But Marsha was feeling the beautiful skating champion inside her head disappear. The music and the arena were fading away. She was nine years old, a little girl with no more wishes in her heart. Her dream had deserted her, and the ugliest skates in the world lay in her lap.

After Christmas, the beautiful skater never appeared whole and beautiful as before. Marsha stuffed Uncle Richard's skates way back in her closet, but it didn't help. If the dream skater came into Marsha's mind at all, her figure skates were too large or the ice would keep melting into water and she would fall in. Marsha couldn't get her dream together any more.

One Saturday morning, several weeks after Christmas vacation, she went to her closet and took out the ugly skates. She sat on her bed and tried them on. They were actually a pretty good fit. She stood up on them. They wobbled. Her ankles wobbled. She clutched the edge of the bed. "It's because there's no ice," she thought. "It'll be all right if there's ice."

At lunchtime she asked Leonard if he would take her to the lagoon. It was a cold and shining day. "Perfect for skating," he announced, and Marsha felt a surge of hope.

When they reached the lagoon, there were many cars parked around it. All sizes of shoes and boots were scattered near the benches on the bank. To Marsha they looked cold and lonely sitting in the snow. The little island in the middle of the lagoon was thick and shapeless with snow-fat trees and bushes. The ice all around it was alive with the activity of skaters, their shouts clear in the cold air.

Marsha felt a shiver of fear nip and tremble in her stomach.

They sat on a cold bench to put on their skates. Leonard laced up rapidly, whistling. Then he stood up impatiently. He waved to some friends skating out on the lagoon.

Marsha finally got her skates laced to the top and tied. She stood up. Her feet didn't feel as if they could fly across the ice. They felt like blocks of wood. "Come on, Marsha," groaned Leonard. She took a step and the skates suddenly slipped away as if they were trying to escape from her feet. Up into the air went her legs. Down into the snow went Marsha.

"Oh, for cryin' out loud," wailed Leonard. But he helped her up and then down the bank to the ice.

From a distance, the frozen lagoon had looked smooth. Close up, Marsha could see that the ice was pitted with the scars of many skates. There were ripples in it and bumps and some long, ragged cracks frozen over. Giggling nervously, Marsha stepped out onto the ice.

Whooooooooosh! Up into the air went Uncle Richard's skates. Down went Marsha onto the ice on her bottom. "Oh, for cryin' out loud," wailed Leonard again. He yanked her up by one arm. But her legs were going in different directions.

Whooooooooosh! Whooooooooosh! And down she went again. "Mar-sha!" complained Leonard. He helped her up again. "Now stand there," he commanded.

Wobbling and swaying, Marsha pushed into her
ankles and stayed in one spot. Her arms were sticking
out on either side, her ankles bent nearly double. She
was practically standing on her ankles.

Leonard grabbed both of her hands. "Now," he
ordered, "keep hold of my hands and keep your
ankles straight, for cryin' out loud." Then, awkwardly, he began to skate backward, pulling Marsha
forward. Her ankles caved in; her ankles bent out.
Back and forth, in and out. She wobbled forward on
the skates of Uncle Richard.

It was no fun. Leonard kept looking around for
his friends. Marsha kept falling down. Her ankles
began to ache dreadfully. Finally Leonard dragged
her to a bench near the little island and left her there.

"Be right back," he said and skated away to talk with his friends.

Marsha sat on the bench alone. She wanted to go home, but she didn't know how she would ever get back across the ice to the snowbank where her boots sat. She dropped her head, full of cold and misery.

A scraping sound, ice skates stopping suddenly, made her look up. A man was standing in front of her, smiling. She was so wrapped up in unhappiness that at first she didn't know him. He was very tall and he had a long, red scarf that trailed over one shoulder. She saw he was leaning toward her, saying something, and then she recognized her Uncle Richard.

He was saying, "Marsha girl, is that you? Why you lookin' so sad?" Marsha saw he was looking at her skates. "Why don't you lace up your skates properly?" he asked. He bent way over and touched them thoughtfully. Marsha could see he was puzzled.

"They were your first skates when you were seven," she explained in a low voice. Uncle Richard knelt down in front of her and took one of her feet in both of his hands. "Yeah," he whispered. "They sure are . . . they sure are. . . ." He looked up at her with delight growing in his face. "Those good old skates." He laughed. Then he began to undo the laces, and Marsha thought he was going to take the skates back. But he was saying, "First off, Marsha, you've got to have your skates laced properly. Your feet are falling out of these. They're laced up all wrong."

Uncle Richard straightened the tongue in her boot. He left the bottom lacings loose so she could wiggle her toes. Then he laced very tightly and evenly across her foot and above her ankle. He tied a knot and laced the rest loosely to the top of the boot. "How does that feel?" he asked after he'd done both feet. It felt great. Like brand-new ankles.

Then he stood her up and began to pull her slowly and evenly across the ice. "Bend your knees, not your middle," he told her. Marsha bent her knees and her middle straightened right up. She was surprised at how easily she could balance now.

After they had gone a short distance, Uncle Richard said, "You do that real easy, so I want to show you some things to practice here while I get some

skating done." First he showed Marsha how to rest her ankles when they got tired. "Stand quiet," he said, "and let your ankles relax right down into your boots . . . right down into the ice. That's important."

Then he said, "Here's something else to practice. Watch close." He pushed forward into one foot and trailed the other behind lightly without touching the ice. "Just bend your knee and lean into it," he said, "nice and easy."

Then he brought the other foot forward and pushed easily into that one. "I push," he said, "and then I glide . . . and then I push with the other foot. And then I glide!" Uncle Richard glided forward, first on one foot and then the other. "Push, glide . . . push, glide. Get it?" Marsha nodded. It made good sense.

"Now you practice that for a while. Practice resting your ankles, too, whenever they get tired. Okay?" Marsha nodded and Uncle Richard skated off, his red scarf trailing. She watched to see if he really could skate as well as her mother said.

Slowly at first Uncle Richard moved across the ice. Then Marsha saw him reach into his pocket and pull out a tiny radio. He held it next to his ear and began to skate to music no one else could hear. Marsha noticed he glided a long time on one foot before he shifted his weight to the other one. Then he made some smooth, neat turns. His speed quickened. He circled into a spin that blurred his entire outline.

The red scarf whipped around him and, as the spin slowed down, gradually began to unwind.

"Oh," breathed Marsha. "Oh, he is fine. He is really fine." Her uncle began skating backward, leaning his ear into the hand that held the radio. He seemed to be sailing, led backward by the music around the lagoon. He never tripped over the humps and cracks in the ice.

People began to stop skating and watch Uncle Richard, who now turned and sped forward. Suddenly he swooped and leapt into a single axel, fine as any Olympic skater. He circled to a halt and began to skate backward again, disappearing around a bend in the little island.

Alone in the middle of the ice, Marsha felt her ankles begin to wobble with worry. She tried resting them. It worked. They stopped wobbling. "But I can't stand here forever," she thought. She tested herself, lifting first one foot and then the other. She took a few timid steps. She skidded a little. She glided a little. She stopped and rested.

Then she took a deep breath, bent her knee, and pushed off into her right foot the way Uncle Richard had done. She glided a little, her body balanced over her skating foot. Then she shifted and pushed into her left foot and glided a shaky distance. It worked! Push, glide . . . push, glide. She brought her legs together and glided on both feet all by herself out alone in the middle of the ice.

She gasped with excitement. It was fun! She tried it again. She pushed off more boldly and glided farther. She did it over again. And again. After a while she rested her ankles. Then she practiced some more . . . push, glide . . . push, glide. She watched her feet. She tried to glide longer on one foot. Push, glide . . . push, glide. She tried to keep her knees bent, her middle straight. Push, glide . . . push, glide.

Suddenly she realized she was at the other end of the lagoon. "My, MY," said a voice behind her. "I thought I left you down at the other end."

It was Uncle Richard. He was turning off his radio and smiling. "How'd you get here?" he asked.

"I push-push-glided," said Marsha. "All by myself. No one helped."

"You foolin' me?" asked Uncle Richard, smiling. "Let's see!"

Wobbling only a little at the beginning, Marsha performed her push, glide . . . push, glide. She remembered to keep her skating knee bent. She skated in a medium-sized circle around him and stopped.

"You are one surprising young lady," said Uncle Richard. "You sure learn fast." Marsha was surprised

herself. He bent down and looked seriously into her face. "You ready for another suggestion?" he asked.

Marsha felt, in that moment, that Uncle Richard could see inside her heart better than anyone. The beautiful figure skater of her dreams floated briefly into her mind, but Marsha didn't have time for her now.

"I want to learn how to skate like you skate," she said. Her voice sounded so little and low to her that she wondered if he'd heard her. But Uncle Richard touched her cheek softly with his fingertips. He looked very thoughtful for a minute. Then he said quietly, "Okay. We'll work on it."

He stood up. "First off, don't leave your body all bundled down inside your coat. Don't watch your feet. Stretch up. Be proud. But not stiff. Look where you're going. Reach after the sky . . . or the moon . . . or a treetop. Okay? You hear? You remember that?" Marsha nodded, her heart pounding.

"You're a natural," said Uncle Richard. "You can be a super fine skater. But you'll have to set your mind to it." Marsha nodded again. She understood. Uncle Richard suddenly laughed out loud. "We'll surprise your momma. Maybe we'll shake up the whole world, okay?" he asked.

"Okay," she said, feeling very warm and sure.

"Now you keep practicing," said Uncle Richard. "Next week we'll have another lesson. I'll talk to your momma. Okay?" Marsha beamed at him. "They're a good old pair of skates." Marsha nodded.

Uncle Richard pushed off. Marsha pushed off after him, her head riding high, her body stretched taller . . . reaching after him, after the sky or the moon or the tops of the trees. Push, glide . . . push, glide. Past her staring brother she skated. Hardly even a wobble. Proud, not stiff. She glided away on the skates of Uncle Richard, taller and taller and taller, never once falling down.

Author

Carol Fenner's books cover many topics. Among them is *Gorilla, Gorilla,* an award-winning science book. The idea for *The Skates of Uncle Richard* came when she saw a small girl in hand-me-down skates being towed across an ice-covered pond.

Dreams

by Langston Hughes

Hold fast to dreams
For if dreams die
Life is a broken-winged bird
That cannot fly.

Hold fast to dreams
For when dreams go
Life is a barren field
Frozen with snow.

HARALD and the GIANT KNIGHT

Written and illustrated by Donald Carrick

Harald lived with his mother, Helga, and his father, Walter, in the valley which spread beneath the castle.

The valley was owned by a baron who lived in the castle, surrounded by his knights. All the farmers in the valley had to give the Baron part of their crops. He, in turn, allowed them to farm his land. Harald's family had farmed the same land for as long as anyone could remember.

Harald's father was a weaver as well as a farmer. He wove eel traps, screens, hats, fences, chairs, and every manner of basket.

One spring morning Harald climbed up to the castle with baskets his father had woven for the castle kitchen. Harald went to the castle as often as he could.

After he delivered the baskets, he wandered through the passageways, exploring the wondrous stone chambers. Many were larger than his home.

Harald was especially fond of the Baron's knights. Knights were different from other folk. They were huge, scarred men who wore leather and metal clothes covered by bright tunics. The knights spoke with deep voices and their clothing creaked and clanked as they walked by. Harald burned to be one of them.

Harald loved the jousts when two knights fought. Best of all were the tournaments. Then he could watch all the Baron's knights clash with all the knights from another castle in a mock battle.

Nothing made Harald happier than to see the galloping horses and the swirling banners, and to hear the clang of sword against shield.

On this particular morning the Baron announced that it was time to begin training for the summer tournaments. A great cheer went up from the knights. They were restless after the long winter they had spent inside the castle.

As Harald walked home, he wished he could train with them.

The next morning, a terrible racket woke Harald. He ran outside to find his father in a fit. Men from the castle were swarming all over their farm. Horns blew. Kettledrums boomed. Tents were going up.

"What's happening?" Harald asked.

"The knights' regular practice fields are flooded, so they've come here to train," his father said.

Harald watched as knights strutted about, shouting a thousand orders.

"We are ruined," groaned Walter. "With all this foolish practice on our fields, how can we plant the spring crops?"

Harald understood how his father felt. Without a harvest, his family would have no food and could not pay the Baron for the use of his land. But at the same time, it was Harald's dream come true. All the knights were right here on his family's farm!

Walter's fields were transformed into a jousting arena in which the knights galloped about on large horses and practiced with their lances.

Since no farming could be done, Harald spent all his time at the knights' camp. Soon he was helping with the horses and tending the fires. Perhaps there was a chance for him to become a knight after all.

The knights' presence changed everything on the farm. There were no more eggs to collect because the constant noise caused the chickens to stop laying. The pigs grew nervous and lost weight.

Harald could not believe it when knights tested their swords by chopping into his father's carefully tended fruit trees. The stone boundary fences his grandfather had built were broken and scattered.

The knights had huge appetites. To fill the camp cookpots they simply took what they wanted from Walter and the other valley farmers. Chickens, ducks, pigs, and goats disappeared in their stewpots and on the roasting spits.

Harald was shocked. He had always thought knights were strong, brave men who spent their time helping people. Instead, he saw them ruin the land and plunder the farms like thieves.

Walter was pleased when Harald announced one day that he was no longer going to the camp. Harald had lost his taste for the knightly life.

To save what little food they had left, Helga gathered it together and put it in a sack. When it was dark, Harald went with his father to hide it. They carried the food down a small path past the knights' camp to a secret cave. Harald had discovered the cave one day last summer while he was picking berries. They hid the food on a high ledge.

When they returned home, no one could sleep so they sat together around their small fire. There seemed to be no answer to their problem.

"If I were big, I'd thrash all the knights and send them running," said Harald. "It's the only thing they understand."

"No one is big enough to do that," answered Helga, "except another knight."

Walter said nothing, but his hands began weaving. The giant shadows his father cast on the wall gave Harald an idea.

"I know how we can get rid of the knights!" he said.

His father stopped weaving. "What do you mean, son?" he asked.

"Well, why can't we make a knight to frighten them?"

"And just how would we do that, Harald?" asked Helga.

"Father is a master weaver, isn't he? He can weave anything. Why can't he weave a giant knight?"

A smile spread over Walter's face. "Let's hear more," he said.

Excitedly they talked late into the night as idea led to idea. By morning they had a plan.

From the next day on, Harald's family spent all their time at the cave weaving their giant. Harald made trip after trip to the cave, bringing Walter great bundles of reeds.

One afternoon rabbit hunters from the camp almost discovered the cave as Harald was about to enter.

"Where are you bound with that bundle, lad?" called the leader, coming closer.

Harald knew that once the dogs got near the entrance to the cave, all would be lost. "Oh, I'm on my way to build a rabbit hutch," he replied, thinking quickly.

"Rabbits! What rabbits?" demanded the hunters.

"The rabbits in the thicket down the ravine. It's full of them," said Harald.

"Well lad, we'll just take a look at this thicket of yours," said the leader, and the hunters marched off.

With each bundle of Harald's reeds, the basket knight grew larger. Harald was very proud of his father's skill. He was sure nothing this large had ever been woven.

"By daylight, he will probably look rather patchy," Walter said. "But by night, after the knights have

finished drinking and are asleep, our knight should
be very frightening."

Helga decided to make a cape for him.

Finally the giant basket knight was finished. He
was almost too large to squeeze through the cave
entrance.

Carefully they mounted the creature on Patience,
their old plow horse, and tied it down.

Walter led Patience down the narrow trail. The knight looked huge but weighed so little that each draft from the valley caught it like a sail. Harald clung to a rope to steady the creature.

At one spot the trees were so close they almost pushed the basket giant off Patience's back. When the knight swayed back and forth it looked even more ghost-like.

"These paths were not made for giants," Harald whispered.

Each small farm along the way had a dog that barked as the giant drew near. Harald started to shiver. What if they were discovered?

Fortunately no one woke.

When they arrived at the edge of camp, the knights were all asleep.

It was Harald's task to enter the camp and untie the horses. He slipped quietly past the tents full of snoring knights. By day he knew the camp, but by night it all seemed different. One mistake could ruin everything.

At last he found the horses and with trembling hands untied the knots. The freed horses began to wander through the camp.

In the light of the early moon, Harald saw the giant loom above the trees.

The moment he appeared, Walter and Helga began a horrific clamor. She clanged pots while he made loud, moaning sounds through a long wooden tube.

That was the signal for Harald to dart from tent to tent, pulling up tent pegs. One after another, the tents collapsed on the sleeping knights.

The bewildered knights awoke in the dark, blanketed by the heavy tents. As they groped free, they tripped over ropes and cracked their shins on tent poles.

Once they were in the open, the mob of bruised, half-clothed knights were startled by the sight of the giant. It seemed to be walking over the trees. It began to shout at them in a deep, creaky voice.

"AWAY WITH YOU. AWAY FROM THE GRAVES OF MY FOREFATHERS. BEGONE, ALL OF YOU, BEFORE THE NEW DAY DAWNS!"

Then, suddenly, the swaying knight seemed to disappear from the sky. The frightened knights were left standing in the shambles of the camp. Actually, the giant had fallen from Patience's back and she trotted away, dragging him behind.

Harald caught up with his parents who were close on Patience's heels. They were busy picking up the bits and pieces that were falling from the giant. There was no time to wonder if their plan had worked until they reached the cave.

129

Dumbfounded, the knights milled about the camp gathering their wits and their horses. No trace of the ghostly giant could be found.

No one wanted to mention the ghost's warning, but one knight had the courage to say, "This camp is a wreck. I think it's time to leave."

"Let's go back to the castle," said a second.

A great sigh of relief came from all sides. Not one knight wanted to stay on and risk seeing the giant again.

Shortly after sunrise Harald, Helga, and Walter watched the band of knights make their way slowly up the hill toward the castle. Helga and Walter hugged each other and cried with relief. Harald, who could not contain himself, jumped for joy.

After a great deal of work, the three of them cleared their fields and planted crops. That fall their harvest was not as big as usual, but it was enough to pay the Baron and feed themselves through the winter.

The next spring Harald and his father were planting once again.

"Listen to what the wind brings us from down the valley," said Walter.

They could hear a faint clanging from the knights at practice on the Baron's field. This time they were but pleasant tinkles to Harald's ears.

Nearby stood a familiar figure. It was a scarecrow, fashioned from the giant's reeds. As it turned with the wind, it almost seemed to smile.

Author

The idea for this story came from Donald Carrick's two young sons. With their encouragement, he studied life in medieval Europe, castles, and peasant farms. Then he wrote and illustrated *Harald and the Giant Knight*.

Mr. Carrick has written and illustrated other books. One that you might enjoy reading is *Morgan and the Artist,* the story of a little painted figure that comes to life. Mr. Carrick has also illustrated over twenty books written by his wife, Carol.

Miss Rumphius

Written and illustrated by Barbara Cooney

The Lupine Lady lives in a small house overlooking the sea. In between the rocks around her house grow blue and purple and rose-colored flowers. The Lupine Lady is little and old. But she has not always been that way. I know. She is my great-aunt, and she told me so.

Once upon a time she was a little girl named Alice, who lived in a city by the sea. From the front stoop she could see the wharves and the bristling masts of tall ships. Many years ago her grandfather had come to America on a large sailing ship.

Now he worked in the shop at the bottom of the house, making figureheads for the prows of ships, and carving Indians out of wood to put in front of cigar stores. For Alice's grandfather was an artist. He painted pictures, too, of sailing ships and places across the sea. When he was very busy, Alice helped him put in the skies.

In the evening Alice sat on her grandfather's knee and listened to his stories of faraway places. When he had finished, Alice would say, "When I grow up, I too will go to faraway places, and when I grow old, I too will live beside the sea."

"That is all very well, little Alice," said her grandfather, "but there is a third thing you must do."

"What is that?" asked Alice.

"You must do something to make the world more beautiful," said her grandfather.

"All right," said Alice. But she did not know what that could be.

In the meantime Alice got up and washed her face and ate porridge for breakfast. She went to school and came home and did her homework.

And pretty soon she was grown up.

Then my Great-aunt Alice set out to do the three things she had told her grandfather she was going to do. She left home and went to live in another city far from the sea and the salt air. There she worked in a library, dusting books and keeping them from getting mixed up, and helping people find the ones they wanted. Some of the books told her about faraway places.

People called her Miss Rumphius now.

Sometimes she went to the conservatory in the middle of the park. When she stepped inside on a wintry day, the warm moist air wrapped itself around her, and the sweet smell of jasmine filled her nose.

"This is almost like a tropical isle," said Miss Rumphius. "But not quite."

So Miss Rumphius went to a real tropical island, where people kept cockatoos and monkeys as pets. She walked on long beaches, picking up beautiful shells. One day she met the Bapa Raja, king of a fishing village.

"You must be tired," he said. "Come into my house and rest."

So Miss Rumphius went in and met the Bapa Raja's wife. The Bapa Raja himself fetched a green coconut and cut a slice off the top so that Miss Rumphius could drink the coconut water inside.

Before she left, the Bapa Raja gave her a beautiful mother-of-pearl shell on which he had painted a bird of paradise and the words, "You will always remain in my heart."

"You will always remain in mine too," said Miss Rumphius.

My great-aunt Miss Alice Rumphius climbed tall mountains where the snow never melted. She went through jungles and across deserts. She saw lions playing and kangaroos jumping. And everywhere she made friends she would never forget.

Finally she came to the Land of the Lotus-Eaters, and there, getting off a camel, she hurt her back.

"What a foolish thing to do," said Miss Rumphius. "Well, I have certainly seen faraway places. Maybe it is time to find my place by the sea."

And it was, and she did.

From the porch of her new house Miss Rumphius watched the sun come up; she watched it cross the heavens and sparkle on the water; and she saw it set in glory in the evening. She started a little garden among the rocks that surrounded her house, and she planted a few flower seeds in the stony ground. Miss Rumphius was *almost* perfectly happy.

"But there is still one more thing I have to do," she said. "I have to do something to make the world more beautiful."

But what? "The world already is pretty nice," she thought, looking out over the ocean.

The next spring Miss Rumphius was not very well. Her back was bothering her again, and she had to stay in bed most of the time.

The flowers she had planted the summer before had come up and bloomed in spite of the stony ground. She could see them from her bedroom window, blue and purple and rose-colored.

"Lupines," said Miss Rumphius with satisfaction. "I have always loved lupines the best. I wish I could plant more seeds this summer so that I could have still more flowers next year."

But she was not able to.

After a hard winter spring came. Miss Rumphius was feeling much better. Now she could take walks again. One afternoon she started to go up and over the hill, where she had not been in a long time.

"I don't believe my eyes!" she cried when she got to the top. For there on the other side of the hill was a large patch of blue and purple and rose-colored lupines!

"It was the wind," she said as she knelt in delight. "It was the wind that brought the seeds from my garden here! And the birds must have helped!"

Then Miss Rumphius had a wonderful idea!

She hurried home and got out her seed catalogues. She sent off to the very best seed house for five bushels of lupine seed.

All that summer Miss Rumphius, her pockets full of seeds, wandered over fields and headlands, sowing lupines. She scattered seeds along the highways and down the country lanes. She flung handfuls of them around the schoolhouse and back of the church. She tossed them into hollows and along stone walls.

Her back didn't hurt her any more at all.

Now some people called her That Crazy Old Lady.

The next spring there were lupines everywhere. Fields and hillsides were covered with blue and purple and rose-colored flowers. They bloomed along the highways and down the lanes. Bright patches lay around the schoolhouse and back of the church. Down in the hollows and along the stone walls grew the beautiful flowers.

Miss Rumphius had done the third, the most difficult thing of all!

My Great-aunt Alice, Miss Rumphius, is very old now. Her hair is very white. Every year there are more and more lupines. Now they call her the Lupine Lady. Sometimes my friends stand with me outside her gate, curious to see the old, old lady who planted the fields of lupines. When she invites us in, they come slowly. They think she is the oldest woman in the world. Often she tells us stories of faraway places.

"When I grow up," I tell her, "I too will go to faraway places and come home to live by the sea."

"That is all very well, little Alice," says my aunt, "but there is a third thing you must do."

"What is that?" I ask.

"You must do something to make the world more beautiful."

"All right," I say.

But I do not know yet what that can be.

Author

Barbara Cooney is famous as an author and an illustrator. Her books for children have won many awards and honors. *Chanticleer and the Fox* won the Caldecott Medal. *Miss Rumphius,* which you have just read, was the co-winner of the 1983 American Book Award for picture books and was named a Notable Children's Trade Book in Social Studies.

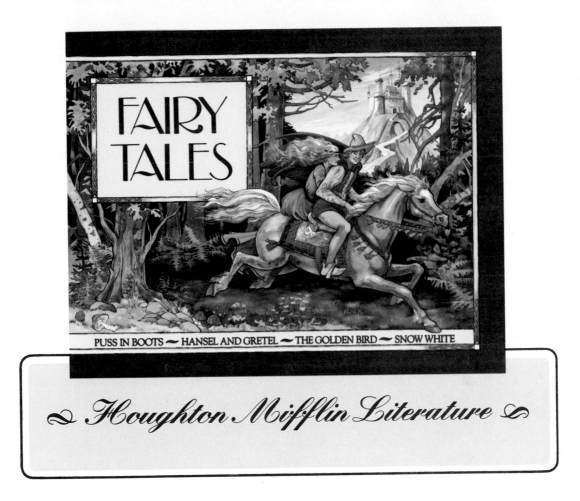

FAIRY TALES

PUSS IN BOOTS ~ HANSEL AND GRETEL ~ THE GOLDEN BIRD ~ SNOW WHITE

~ *Houghton Mifflin Literature* ~

Are the hopes and dreams in fairy tales different from those of Marsha, Harald, and Miss Rumphius?

See what you think as you read this book of fairy tales: *Puss in Boots* by Charles Perrault; *Hansel and Gretel*, *The Golden Bird*, and *Snow White* by the Brothers Grimm.

143

Searching
for Clues

The Green Thumb Thief

by Mary Blount Christian

Illustrated by Martin Cottom

I tore open the newspaper and found our ad.

MYSTERIES SOLVED.
A DOLLAR A DAY PLUS EXPENSES.
DEKE KING AND ASSOCIATE,
THE UNDERCOVER KIDS.

My associate, Snitch, moaned, "I hope it gets us some business. We spent all our money on this ad." He pulled his ear. Snitch always pulls his ear when he's upset.

The phone rang. I answered. It was the first call on our ad. A woman said her name was Flora Greene. She told me she was desperate.

Snitch and I pedaled our bikes straight to her house. The yard was filled with shrubs and plants. It looked like a jungle. Flora Greene asked us inside. Behind her a small piece of fluff rumbled. It looked the same at both ends — like a dust mop in search of a handle.

"That a dog?" I asked, making a wild guess.

"Of course," she said. "That's Hercules." At the mention of its name, the fluff wiggled. I stooped to pat it.

Flora Greene took us through the house to the backyard. She had a greenhouse there full of plants and flowers.

"I need you to take care of these while I'm gone," she said. "And Hercules, too."

Snitch yanked on his ear.

"But we are detectives, not babysitters," I explained. "Undercover kids. We solve mysteries."

"I want to STOP a mystery before it happens," she said, shoving a newspaper toward me. She'd circled a headline in ink.

RARE, EXPENSIVE PLANTS STOLEN.
GREEN THUMB THIEF AT LARGE.
POLICE BAFFLED, FIND NO CLUES.

The paper said there was one suspect — a plant shop owner at the flea market. But none of the stolen plants could be identified, so the police had to let him go. Without positive identification, they had no proof he was the thief.

"I will pay you twice your usual fee," Flora Greene said.

I glanced at Snitch. He nodded eagerly. I shrugged. "I suppose we can think of ourselves as sort of bodyguards," I said.

I took out my notebook. "What do you want us to do?" I asked.

She touched a floppy looking plant. "First you'll have to get to know my plants. This is Emily. Say hello to Emily."

I felt my face growing red and backed up into a big potted plant. "Ouch!" I cried. Something had pinched my arm.

"That's Venus," the woman said. "Don't mind her. She is sometimes very naughty and bites people."

I glanced around for Snitch. He was tugging like crazy on his ear.

"Plants need to be talked to," Flora Greene continued. "They can tell if you don't like them."

I nodded. It would be embarrassing to talk to plants, but I thought of the double money we'd earn.

I wrote the plants' names down. I drew pictures of the different leaves.

"Do they — er — all eat at the same time?" I asked.

"Oh my, no! Emily is always thirsty. She needs water every day. But Samantha here takes water just once a week."

I wrote down information about Hercules, too.

On the way home, I told Snitch, "We'll never remember how much water each plant gets. We need a reminder."

"Reminder?" Snitch said. He thought a moment. He pulled on his ear. "You know how people tie a piece of string around their finger to remember something?"

My detective instinct told me he was on to something. "Go on," I said.

"Well, maybe we could tie yarn on the plants," Snitch said. "Different colors."

"Oh, you mean like a code?" I asked. "Different colors of yarn would let us know to water plants on different days?"

Snitch nodded. I could tell he was pleased with himself.

The next day Snitch and I took pieces of colored yarn to Flora Greene's. We put red yarn on the plants that needed water every day, blue yarn on the ones that needed water every other day, and green yarn on the ones that needed water just once a week.

"I'll water the plants," I told Snitch. "You and Hercules stand guard in the front yard." I knew we had to be careful with the Green Thumb Thief on the loose.

Pretty soon Snitch and Hercules came back inside. I looked at Hercules. "How did he get so dirty?" I asked Snitch.

"He fell in the hole out front," Snitch answered.

"There isn't any hole out front," I said. "At least, there wasn't when we got here."

"There is now." Snitch yanked on his ear.

I went outside to check. Sure enough, there was a hole where a big plant used to be. Someone must have stolen it while we were busy tying yarn on the plants inside.

"The Green Thumb Thief has struck right under the noses of the Undercover Kids," I said. "We have got to find that thief and save our honor!"

"The job might be dangerous," Snitch said.

"We'll need to go undercover," I decided. "Put on a disguise and meet me back here."

"What kind of disguise?" Snitch asked.

"Something to do with gardens and stuff," I said, leaping on my bike.

I searched my attic and found the perfect disguise. It was a good thing I had played an oak tree in the school play. Who would suspect an oak tree?

I hurried back to Flora Greene's. I decided to guard the front yard — there were still some valuable plants left. I kept watch through my knothole and waited for Snitch. When I saw him, I couldn't believe my eyes. He was pedaling down the street dressed like a chicken.

"A chicken?" I yelled. "I tell you to disguise yourself for the garden and you dress up like a chicken?"

His feathers ruffled as he shrugged. "I couldn't find any other costume. Besides, chickens get in gardens."

"Oh, brother," I said.

Snitch settled down on the ground near me. Pretty soon we heard a whimper coming from the backyard.

"Is that Hercules?" I asked. Snitch looked at me. "It sounds like something's wrong," he said.

We ran to the back of the house. The greenhouse door was open. Emily's shelf was empty. So was Samantha's. Lots of other plants were gone, too.

"Hercules?" Snitch whispered. "Where are you?"

The poor little dog crawled out from behind a big pot. He was shaking all over. A piece of cloth hung from his front tooth.

"Good dog, Hercules," I said. "I bet that belongs to the thief." Hercules wiggled.

I crammed the cloth in my pocket, underneath my tree trunk. Snitch scooped up Hercules. We looked for more clues.

There were tire tracks in the alley. But they vanished a block away.

"What would a thief do with all those plants?" Snitch asked.

"Sell them?" I said. "Hold them for ransom?"

"There's a shop at the flea market that sells plants," Snitch said. "The newspaper story said the owner was under suspicion, but none of the people robbed could positively identify their plants."

We went to the flea market. Snitch walked up and down one aisle. Plants were everywhere. But they all looked alike. Then I saw a familiar looking floppy plant. "Emily!" I yelled.

A big guy came over to me. He stared down at me and Hercules. "Hey," he said, snickering. "That's pretty cute! This little doggie has got his own tree!" Then he whispered, "Get lost, tree, before I turn you into toothpicks."

By that time Snitch had found a police officer. He brought her over. She smiled at me. "I hear that you've identified one of your stolen plants," she said. "Most plants can't talk the way you can. So how are you able to tell which plant is yours?"

I stood tall inside my trunk. "Some plants can talk," I said. I pointed to Emily's red yarn and to the drawing I'd made of her in my notebook. "This is Emily," I said. "We put red yarn on her so that we could remember to water her every day."

"He probably planted the evidence," the man snarled.

"*Planted*?" the officer said. "Are you trying to be funny?" She turned to me. "That is not bad proof. But if this guy claims he bought the plants from someone else, we'll need more evidence."

Hercules growled. I remembered the cloth I'd found in his mouth. I showed it to the police officer.

The plant shop owner grinned. "He's changed clothes," Snitch whispered to me. "We can't prove a thing."

"Let's find out how good a detective your little friend is," the police officer said. She held the piece of cloth in front of Hercules's nose. His nose quivered. The plant shop owner backed away.

Suddenly Hercules bounded into the booth. He sniffed all around it. He tugged at a pair of pants that were stuffed behind some flower pots.

The officer held them up. There was a hole in them. The piece of cloth fit perfectly. Splotches of Hercules's fur were on the pants. "Shedding is Hercules's best trick," I said.

A reporter came to the flea market. He took a picture of Snitch and me and Hercules with Emily.

The officer arrested the Green Thumb Thief. She helped us get Emily and the other plants back to the greenhouse.

When Flora Greene got home from vacation, she saw the picture of us in the newspaper. She said that was the best picture Emily ever had taken. She paid us *three* times our regular fee and said we were worth it.

Not a bad day's work for a dog, a tree, and a big chicken!

Author

Mary Blount Christian is well known for her entertaining mysteries for young readers. Her three children have given her ideas for the more than thirty children's books she has written. In her home state of Texas, she created a weekly educational TV show on children's books that has been shown nationwide.

DIGGING UP DINOSAURS

Written and illustrated by Aliki

And putting them together again.

Have you ever seen dinosaur skeletons in a museum? I have. I visit them all the time. I went again yesterday. I saw APATOSAURUS. I saw CORYTHOSAURUS. I saw IGUANODON and TRICERATOPS. I like to say their names.

STEGOSAURUS was just where I had left it. And TYRANNOSAURUS REX looked as fierce as ever. TYRANNOSAURUS used to scare me. I still can't believe how big it is. Just its head is almost twice my size.

IGUANODON
PLANT-EATER

TRICERATOPS
(HORNED DINOSAUR)
PLANT-EATER

I recognize IGUANODON by its horn-thumbs.

Tri means three.

THREE HORNS!

And now...

I'm not afraid of dinosaurs anymore. Sometimes I call them "you bag of bones" under my breath. I can spend hours looking at them. I used to wonder where they came from and how they got into the museum. But now I know.

Dinosaurs lived millions of years ago. A few of them were as small as birds, but most were enormous.

DIPLODOCUS

COMPSOGNATHUS

BRACHIOSAURUS

Some dinosaurs ate plants. Some dinosaurs ate the meat of other dinosaurs, and some may even have eaten the eggs of other dinosaurs.

Dinosaurs lived everywhere. They lived on every continent in the world. Then they died out. No one knows for sure why they became extinct. But they did. There hasn't been a dinosaur around for 65 million years.

ORNITHOMIMUS

TYRANNOSAURUS

Until about 200 years ago, no one knew anything about dinosaurs. Then people began finding things in rock. They found large footprints. They found huge, mysterious bones and strange teeth. People were finding fossils.

Fossils are a kind of diary of the past. They are the remains of plants and animals that died long ago. Instead of rotting or crumbling away, the remains were preserved, and slowly turned to stone.

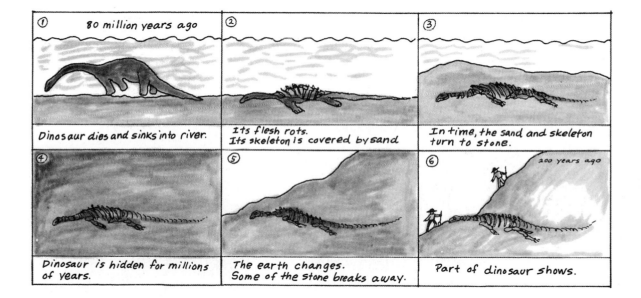

① 80 million years ago
Dinosaur dies and sinks into river.

② Its flesh rots. Its skeleton is covered by sand

③ In time, the sand and skeleton turn to stone.

④ Dinosaur is hidden for millions of years.

⑤ The earth changes. Some of the stone breaks away.

⑥ 200 years ago
Part of dinosaur shows.

Fossils tell about life on earth long ago. Everything we know about dinosaurs comes from studying fossils.

1822

Mary Ann Mantell found
the first dinosaur fossils
in England.

She discovered some
giant fossil teeth.

1825

Her husband, Gideon Mantell,
named the animal
IGUANODON, or IGUANA-
TOOTH.
Nine years later he
found an IGUANODON
skeleton.

1841

Richard Owen named
the giant reptiles
DINOSAURIA.

Fossil hunters found more and more big bones in different parts of the world. Scientists studied the fossils. They said the bones and teeth and footprints all belonged to a group of giant reptiles that lived on earth for millions of years. The giants were named DINOSAURIA, or TERRIBLE LIZARD.

What finds these were! People crowded into museums to see them. But the dinosaur bones didn't just get up and walk there. They had to be dug out of the ground, slowly and patiently.

Even today, digging up dinosaurs is not an easy job. A team of experts must work together.

This is how fossil hunters work.

First, they have to find a dinosaur. They search along riverbanks and in quarries. They climb up high cliffs, and down into steep canyons. With luck, someone spots a fossil bone poking through the rock. The site is covered with a tent, and the work begins.

Sometimes the fossil is buried so deep, the rock around it has to be drilled or blasted. Tons of rubble are carted away. Scientists chip at the rock close to the fossil. They brush away the grit. They have to be very careful.

169

As soon as a bone is uncovered, it is brushed with
shellac. The shellac helps hold the bone together, so
it won't crumble. Then the bone is numbered.

Sometimes a skeleton has to be cut apart so that it can be moved. The draftsman draws each bone in its exact position, and the photographer takes pictures. That way, there can be no mix-up later, when someone tries to put the skeleton together.

When the bones are ready to be moved, they are carefully wrapped. Small bones are wrapped in tissue paper and put into boxes or sacks. Large bones are left half-buried in rock. They will be dug out later, in the museum.

These fossils are covered with a plaster cast, just as a broken leg is. Each bone is then packed in straw, put in crates, and taken to the museum.

At the museum, scientists unwrap the fossil. They finish digging it out of the rock. They study the bones. They compare the bones to other dinosaur bones. They compare them to the bones of other animals.

First, the parts of the fossil that show are covered with wet tissue paper, and then with strips of burlap dipped in wet plaster. Then the whole piece is wrapped in the same way. When the plaster dries, it becomes very hard. The tissue paper covering makes the cast easier to remove later.

They try to figure out what size and shape the dinosaur was. They try to find out how the dinosaur stood and walked, and what it ate.

If there are enough bones, scientists are able to build a complete skeleton. A frame is made in the shape of the dinosaur to support the bones. The bones are wired together, one by one. They are held in place with pieces of metal.

Scientists dig out the fossil in many different ways. They use a hammer and chisel, fine needles, power tools like a dentist's drill, special sandblasting machines, or even chemicals that dissolve the rock but do not harm the fossil.

If any bones are missing, plastic or fiberglass ones are made to replace them. You can hardly tell the new bones from the old.

After many months the work is complete. The dinosaur skeleton looks just as it once did.

Until recently, only a few museums had dinosaurs. Then scientists learned to make copies of the skeletons. The copy is hard to make. It takes a long time. The original skeleton has to be taken completely apart, bone by bone. A mold is made for each bone. The new pieces are made of fiberglass. A fiberglass dinosaur is just as scary as the original, but much stronger and lighter.

Now museums all over the world have dinosaur skeletons. And many people can spend hours looking at them, the way I do.

Each bone has a top and bottom mold.

The original bone is covered with rubber latex and an outer coating of fiberglass to hold the rubber stiff. This is peeled off the bone to form the mold. The inside is brushed with resin and filled with fiberglass. Many dinosaurs can be made from the same molds.

Author

Aliki, Mrs. Franz Brandenberg, is the author of over twenty children's books, some of them award winners. She has been an art teacher and a book illustrator. Her two young children introduced her to dinosaurs. Much later, when they were grown up, she wrote the book she wished she had had then to answer some of their questions.

THE MUSEUM

by Jack Prelutsky

I went to the museum,
it was filled with things to see,
there were rocks and gems and fossils
and a stuffed menagerie.

There were arrowheads and armor
and a mummy in a tomb,
I even saw a great blue whale
that took up one whole room.

I liked my afternoon there,
but I would have liked it more
if only they had let me pet
just one small dinosaur.

The Buried Treasure

Retold by Djemma Bider

Illustrated by
Kristina Rodanas

Once upon a time, an old man lived in the Caucasus Mountains. He had a garden, and he worked in it all day long. He loved his garden very much.

His three sons loved the garden too. But they were lazy fellows and did not care for hard work. And hoeing, digging, planting, and carrying water is very hard work.

Still, each of the sons did do something now and then. The oldest went fishing. The middle son went hunting. And the youngest son took care of a neighbor's horses. But they did not bring much money home to their wives and children.

The years passed, and one day the father became too old to work. He called his sons to him and said, "Dear children, I will tell you a secret. I happen to know there is a treasure buried in my garden. You will inherit this garden after I die. If you keep digging in the earth, sooner or later you will find the treasure."

Not long after that the old man died. The sons grieved for their father. They buried him with great honor.

After a while they gathered their families, relatives, and friends together to discuss what should be done about the treasure.

"What if we have to dig up the entire garden before we find the treasure?" the oldest son said. "There is no way we can guess where it lies."

"Who knows how deep the treasure is buried? It will be such hard work," said the middle son.

The third son said, "What you say is true. Yet how wonderful it would be to find this treasure. We would never have to work again!"

They started to dream aloud . . .

They would trade some of the gold they found for money and buy wonderful things, and when they ran out of money, there would always be enough gold to trade again. All day long they could sit cross-legged in a tavern, chatting with friends, drinking strong tea, and smoking long pipes. What a life it would be!

So, they got down to work.

One morning while they were digging, their favorite uncle passed by. "Good day, my nephews," he said. "How is it coming along? I wish you good luck."

"It's hard going, dear Uncle," said the oldest. "And we certainly can use your good wishes. Who knows how long it will take us to find the treasure?"

"Indeed, who knows?" replied the uncle. "But since you are digging in the earth anyway, why don't you plant some seeds? Stop by my house and I will give you some."

The uncle gave the brothers plenty of seeds: pumpkin and melon seeds, cabbage and carrot seeds, parsley and pea seeds.

And he gave them seeds for flowers: marigolds and morning glories, petunias and poppies, sweet williams and snapdragons.

And that was not all. He gave them saplings for apple, plum, apricot, and cherry trees, so that someday they could have an orchard.

The brothers did as their uncle had advised. They planted the seeds as they dug the soil. When they wanted to plant the saplings, they made especially deep holes. They watered the soil often.

Day after day they worked under the hot sun. Their muscles grew stronger and their skin became so tanned that their teeth and the whites of their eyes sparkled like the snow on the Caucasian mountaintops. At noontime their wives brought them goat's

cheese, flat bread, sour milk, and cakes of rice and honey.

As time passed, the brothers began to love their work. They talked less and less about the treasure; often they forgot the reason they had started digging. The beautiful results of their months of labor began pushing and peeping through the earth.

At summer's end, the brothers had a fine harvest. They brought their vegetables and flowers to the market, and they were the best! Their watermelons were the reddest and ripest. How sweet were their Persian melons — they had a wonderful aroma. And what flowers their wives sold! Wealthy women, even those from faraway mountain villages, came to buy them.

Year after year, the brothers worked hard in spring and summer, and in autumn they reaped a rich crop. When the villagers celebrated harvest time, the merriest parties were always held at the homes of the three brothers.

And so the three brothers realized how wise their father had been. They understood what their father had meant when he said that sooner or later they would find a treasure in the earth.

Author

In *The Buried Treasure,* Djemma Bider has retold an old folktale from the Caucasus Mountains in Russia. Ms. Bider was born in Russia and speaks several languages.

Ms. Bider has translated stories and poems of well-known Russian writers into English. She has also translated some stories of Isaac Singer and others from English into Russian. One of her translations from Russian that you might enjoy reading is *How I Hunted the Little Fellows.* It was named a Notable Book by the American Library Association.

George Washington's
Breakfast

by Jean Fritz

Paul Galdone
drew the pictures

Houghton Mifflin Literature

In the stories you just read, searching for clues
was important. In this story, something is puzzling
George Washington Allen, and he won't be satisfied
until he finds the answer. You, too, will get caught up
in the exciting search for clues as you read *George
Washington's Breakfast* by Jean Fritz.

5

Journeys

Owney
The Traveling Dog

Excerpts from the book by Lynn Hall

Illustrated by Jeremy Guitar

It was a cold, snowy evening, but the streets of Albany, N.Y., were crowded with carriages drawn by fine horses. Women in long skirts looked into bright store windows. Men smiled and nodded to one another and called, "Merry Christmas."

Through the lines of carriages came the post office wagon. It was bringing large sacks of mail from the railroad station to the post office.

Even that speed was almost too much for the puppy under the wagon.

He was a very small brown puppy, and he had to run to keep up with the horses. This place, under the wagon, was safe. It was the only safety the puppy had found from the dangers of the city streets. And the wagon kept the snow off him, though he was already so cold and wet it hardly mattered.

But worse than being cold and tired was being hungry. The hunger made the puppy weak. It frightened him. Even though he was very young, he understood that hunger could kill him.

He fell. Part of him just wanted to lie there and give up. But the stronger part of him said NO.

He got up and ran until he was under the mail wagon again.

Suddenly they were going down a steep hill. Then it was dark, quiet, and warm! The wagon stopped, and so did the pup.

Soon there were people around the wagon. The puppy saw black boots, gray pants legs, and huge gray bags, marked U.S. MAIL.

There was something welcoming about the big gray bags. In the back of the puppy's mind was something big and soft and warm. It was something that had given him life and food.

When all the black boots were on one side of the wagon, the pup trotted out on the other side and climbed up onto the nearest gray bag. It was not as soft as it looked. In fact, it had bumps and corners sticking up everywhere. But the pup was too sleepy to care. It was warm here, and he didn't need to run any more.

He curled up and slept.

The sharp hunger pain in his stomach woke him.

Hours had passed. His brown coat was dry now, and he was thoroughly warm. When he lifted his head, he found that someone had put a woolen scarf over him. He sat up and blinked.

The horses and wagon were gone now. He was in a large dim room that was filled with stacks of gray bags. Several men were working at tables, sorting mail.

Closer to the pup, two men sat eating sandwiches and watching him.

"He's awake," James said.

"It's about time," Buck answered. "I was beginning to worry. He's too young to be out in this weather."

The pup didn't know what the words meant, but he knew kindness. And he very definitely knew the smell of food!

He fell down the side of the sack, but landed running. He went to the nearest man, and the miracle happened. He was given food — a crust of the sandwich. It was gone before he'd even tasted it.

"He's starving, the poor little devil," Buck said. Buck gave the pup the rest of the sandwich — meat and all.

"What can we do with him?" James asked. "We can't put him out on the streets. He'd never live."

Buck scratched his head. "Well, I can't take him home. King would be jealous if I brought another dog into the house. He thinks he owns the place."

"And I can't," James said. "No pets are allowed in our apartment. He's a cute little beggar, though, isn't he?"

They thought some more. Then James said, "Let's just keep him here. He can be our mascot. It won't take much to feed him. And he'll be good company, especially at night."

And so the pup stayed on. Buck and James named him Owney, and they fixed a bed for him in a warm corner of the office. The bed was an empty mail sack, folded over. The other men on the night shift soon found out about the pup. They began bringing extra food in their dinner pails. Before long the thin little dog was a fat and happy puppy. He had 30 loving owners.

By the time spring came to Albany, Owney was large enough, and curious enough, to go exploring. He trotted up and down all the streets near the

post office. He spent a lot of time in the barn where the post office horses and wagons were kept. Now that he was quick enough to dodge their feet, he lost his fear of the horses. They became his friends.

In fact there was nothing that the brown pup was afraid of. He had a fine home in the post office. He had all the food he wanted, and all the company he wanted. When he needed to be loved, there were willing hands to pet him.

One bright day in June, Owney came home from a visit to the barn. Now he wanted to have a nap, but he found that his bed was gone. He went to the corner where it had been and stood there, with his head cocked to one side.

One of the men saw him and said, "Sorry, Owney. We were short of mail bags for this afternoon's mail. We had to use yours. I'll fix you another bed when I get a minute."

Owney didn't understand the words. So he turned around and trotted out into the loading area. The wagon for the afternoon mail stood by the dock. Two men were loading the bags.

Owney stopped. He stared up at the loaded mail bags for a moment. Then he leaped onto the dock and from there into the wagon.

"Get down from there, Owney," one of the men called. But the man was busy, and he didn't watch what Owney did.

The little dog climbed up, around, and over the gray mail bags until he found the one that was his. It was fat with letters instead of folded flat, as it was supposed to be. But it was Owney's bed. He circled three times on his sack and then settled down for a nap.

Soon the wagon moved away from the dock. Owney slept through the trip down the streets of Albany. He woke up only when the wagon stopped at the railroad station. Close beside the wagon was a freight car. It was one of more than a hundred cars that made up the long, long train.

No one noticed Owney when he jumped down. The pup trotted up and down the railway platform and stared at the train. It was the biggest thing he had ever seen. Its wheels held faint smells from many distant places. Owney grew almost dizzy with the excitement of it all.

He came back to the wagon just in time to see his own gray bag as it was tossed inside the freight car.

Owney got a running start and jumped up into the car.

"Scram, you mutt," someone shouted. "Darned old stray dogs!"

But Owney just moved around the mail bags. The man was too busy to chase him. Owney found his bag and settled into a soft place on the top of it. Then something whistled. Something whished and whooshed and chugged, and the train began to move.

Owney sat up, pleasantly surprised. He was going on another ride. The train clicked and clacked and picked up speed.

The door of the mail car had been left partly open. Owney slid down the pile of bags and sat beside the door. Things he had never seen before flashed past. He sniffed the animal smells, the green smells, the

earth smells. His head moved from side to side, faster and faster, as he tried to see everything that was going past. His tail wagged faster and faster with excitement.

Suddenly someone was standing behind him. He was an old man, a stranger. But he wore the same gray uniform that Owney's other men wore. So Owney gave him a wag and went back to watching through the door.

"Would you look here," the man said to another man, who was sorting mail at a table. "We've got ourselves a little passenger."

Through the rest of the long journey, the men petted Owney and played with him. They even shared their suppers with him. It was just like being at home for Owney, except there was the additional excitement of the outdoors flashing by. The noise of the wheels beneath the car was part of the excitement, too.

Late that night, the train stopped, and the men began unloading the mail bags.

"What should we do about the dog?" one man asked.

The old man said, "We'd better send him back to Albany on the 2:15 train. He must belong to somebody there."

Then the old man wrote a note and fastened it to Owney's collar. The note said, "Your dog rode to Buffalo with us. We're sending him back." When the mail car of the southbound 2:15 was loaded and ready to leave for Albany, the old man handed Owney to another man. "Be sure to put him off at Albany," he said.

And so, at midmorning the next day, Owney rode into the Albany post office atop the load of incoming mail sacks.

At first he was so glad to be back among his friends. James and Buck and the others had missed him. But after a few days he began to think about the fun he had on that train trip.

One day before long another wagon of mail went to the depot. In the back were seventeen gray mail sacks and one small brown dog. The little dog had a gleam in his bright black eyes.

This time the train went south, then west. It was five days before Owney got back to Albany, but he wasn't worried. All around him were the familiar mail sacks and kind men in postal uniforms. They fed him, and sometimes they talked about him.

"That's Owney," one man would say to another. "He belongs to the boys in the Albany office. They sent out telegrams to all the stations asking to have him sent back if we found him."

"But how did he get in our mail car?"

"When we weren't looking, I guess. He just likes to ride trains. He was on the 8:10 out of Albany. They took him off at Cleveland and put him on the northbound 3:08. They passed him on to us. We'll put him off at Rochester, and the men there will put him on the 9:19 back to Albany."

When he got back this time, Owney was even less happy to stay home. It was as though home was no longer just the Albany post office. Home was anywhere there were mail sacks and men in gray uniforms to take care of him.

His collar now carried a metal tag with Owney's name on it and the words, "Please return to Albany Post Office."

Although he couldn't know it, Owney's fame spread throughout every post office in the United States. The men hoped to find him among the sacks whenever a load of mail came in. Each place that Owney went, the workers gave him a tag with the name of their post office on it.

In a short time Owney's collar was so heavy with tags that it made him tired to hold up his head.

The collar brought him a lot of attention when people were around. But when he was alone, it was just too heavy to wear. So he learned to pull it off with his front paws. Then, when he felt the train slowing for a station, he worked his head back through the collar. As the door opened he would jump down from the train in all his jingling glory.

One day a package came addressed to the Postmaster, Albany Post Office. It was from Mr. Rodman Wanamaker, the postmaster general of the United States.

Inside was a beautiful harness made of soft, soft leather. "For Owney's tags," the note said.

As the years passed, the harness held many tags. There were ones from Mexico and Alaska. There were other tags from every state. Back and forth across the nation, trains rattled and roared. From the crack in the mail car door peered two bright black eyes in a shaggy face.

Late one evening, when Owney was seven years old, he was at home in Albany. Buck and James talked about his travels as the men ate their midnight supper.

"There's only one place Owney hasn't been," Buck said thoughtfully.

"Where's that?"

Buck looked up at James and slowly began to smile. "Around the world."

Three hours later Owney was aboard the west-bound 3:50. On his back was his traveling packet with his blanket and comb and brush. There was also a note that said, "Owney wants to go around the world."

Three days later Owney woke from a nap and sniffed the air. Behind him was the city of Tacoma, Washington. Before him was the ocean, with its salt smells. Owney was lying on mail bags that were bouncing toward the gangplank of a ship.

The little brown dog jumped down and watched with surprise.

"Go ahead, Owney," called the men around him. "You're going for a boat ride this time, instead of a train ride."

He cocked his head and stared at the mail bags as they disappeared into the ship. This was new to him. But the ship smelled of exciting places. He gave one sassy bark to the men who watched him. Then he trotted up the gangplank.

The S.S. *Victoria* was a huge, beautiful ship. She roared and hummed and pulled away from the dock. Crowds of people stood on the deck waving good-bye, so no one noticed the little brown dog.

Owney sat beside their feet and looked down at the water far, far below. This was different from the fields and cities that flashed past the train doors. The ship roared and hummed, instead of clacking as the train did.

But he was traveling, and the wind brought exciting new smells to his nose. Owney wagged his tail, unnoticed, and settled down to enjoy the trip.

After a while he grew sleepy from watching the waves. He was just closing his eyes when two huge hands picked him up. The man wore a uniform, but it was white. It was not the gray uniform of Owney's post office men.

The man in white carried Owney as though the little dog were dirty. When he stopped he was in front of a bigger man, also in a white uniform.

"Here he is, captain, just like I told you. A stray dog, on our ship." The man sounded angry.

The captain frowned down at Owney. "How in thunder did that mutt get on board? Take him below. We'll send him back to shore on the next Coast Guard boat."

"Yes, sir," said the man who held Owney.

The captain turned to go, but stopped and looked again at Owney's harness. He bent down to read the tags. Suddenly he smiled.

"This is no mutt," he said. "This is Owney. I read a story about him in the newspaper. This dog has done more traveling than you have. Take him below and feed him. Then let him have the run of the entire ship. Welcome aboard, Owney." The captain's huge hand covered Owney's head.

The days that followed were full and happy days for Owney. He ate delicious food at the captain's table in the fancy dining room. He trotted along the decks and was patted and admired by the passengers. At night he slept in the mail room in the lower part of the ship. There he was comfortably surrounded by his mail bags and his gray-suited men.

When the *Victoria* docked in Japan, huge crowds were waiting to welcome it. The captain stood holding Owney under one arm. Suddenly he said to the steward, "Look, there comes the royal party."

"The emperor himself?" the steward asked.

"No," the captain said. "The ambassador is heading the party. I wired the newspapers that Owney was aboard. The emperor must have heard about him and sent the ambassador."

When the engines were finally still and the gangplank down, the ambassador, followed by palace guards, came aboard.

He saw Owney in the captain's arms, and he bowed low. "This is the famous traveling dog from America," he said. The ambassador held out toward Owney an important-looking paper. "We welcome you to Japan, traveling dog. We give you this honorary passport as a token of the friendship between my country and yours."

Similar honors waited for Owney in Shanghai and Singapore. Then he sailed through the Suez Canal to Port Said, then to Gibraltar and the Azores, and finally across the Atlantic Ocean to New York. In New York friendly hands put him on the fastest train to Albany.

On December 23rd Owney trotted into the Albany post office and leaped into Buck's arms. He had circled the world in 132 days.

If Owney was famous before, he was even more famous now. Photographers and reporters came from the big newspapers.

"What will happen to him next?" one reporter asked Buck. "Will he stay home?"

"Probably," Buck said. "Owney's not a young dog anymore."

The men laughed fondly and smiled down at Owney.

Two days later a fast freight whistled across the plains of Kansas. From the crack in the door, two bright black eyes looked out.

Author

Lynn Hall knows a great deal about animals, especially dogs. She has worked with them in professional dog shows. She has also been a veterinarian's assistant.

In the middle of woods and hills in Iowa, she has her own kennels, where she raises show dogs. Ms. Hall has written over thirty books, all about animals.

Travel

by Edna St. Vincent Millay

The railroad track is miles away,
    And the day is loud with voices speaking,
Yet there isn't a train goes by all day
    But I hear its whistle shrieking.

All night there isn't a train goes by,
    Though the night is still for sleep and dreaming
But I see its cinders red on the sky,
    And hear its engine steaming.

My heart is warm with the friends I make,
    And better friends I'll not be knowing,
Yet there isn't a train I wouldn't take,
    No matter where it's going.

An Oak Tree Dies and a Journey Begins

by Louanne Norris and
Howard E. Smith, Jr.

Illustrated by Paul Breeden

A big, old oak tree grew on the bank of a river. During the summer its green leaves hid many of its branches. Other branches were dead and bare. Light gray bark covered most of its trunk. Once the oak had had firm, pale brown wood under its bark. But over the years parts of it had rotted and turned gray. The tree had a few large holes in its trunk. And here and there branches had broken off.

One autumn night the biggest storm in years shook the old oak tree. Its yellow and brown leaves quivered. Many of them were whipped away. The tree swayed and creaked. The wind pulled at its roots. The wind blew very hard. Some of the roots that were rotten broke, and the tree fell to the bank.

All winter long the oak tree lay on the bank. Its top branches lay in the river. Ice formed on them. Many twigs broke. The rest of its leaves fell off.

Close-up of leaf and acorn from white oak tree

Oak tree on riverbank

211

In the spring more rain than usual fell. The water rose. The river flooded and spilled over the bank. The water became so deep that the tree began to move. It floated downstream with the current.

The swift flowing water carried the tree past forests and farms. The tree almost got caught at a bend in the river, but the current moved it along. Branches, bottles, and an empty rowboat bobbed along beside it.

The racing water pushed the tree into the sandy shore of a small island. The water forced the tree's dead roots into the sand, and the roots held. The flood

Tree floating downstream

stopped. The water went down, and the tree stayed.

Where the sun shone on the tree, the wet wood dried out. The bark split in many places, and most of it fell off. The wood turned gray, stiff, and hard. Some of the driest parts looked almost chalk white in the sunlight.

In the shaded areas near the ground, the wood was damp. Molds and mushrooms grew there, and sow bugs lived in the damp wood.

Not all of the tree was on land. Many of its upper branches were under the water. They turned very dark, but they did not rot.

A female raccoon found a hole in the dried-out part of the tree. During the day she slept in the hole. At night she went hunting along the river for frogs, fishes, and small birds. She dipped the food in the river to soften it so that she could easily swallow it. In the winter she mated with a male raccoon. The following spring she had babies.

Frogs swam in the still water near the tree. They hopped up onto the branches. Their eyes blinked, and they turned their heads. When black snakes crawled along the trunk of the tree, the frogs leapt into

Raccoon in hole in tree

Snakes and frogs on trunk of tree

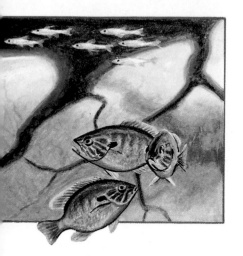

Minnows and sunfish swimming near tree

the water. When dragonflies flew by, the frogs snapped at them with their long tongues.

Minnows darted under the tree's branches. Yellow perch, pickerel, suckers, and other fish swam nearby. Sometimes big river bass hid in the dark shadows of the tree. When smaller fish swam by, the bass swam out and swallowed them.

Two children often sat on the tree and fished. They knew that bass hid among the branches. From time to time they caught one.

The tree lay on the island for a few years.

But one spring heavy rains fell again, and the river flooded. The water got very deep and moved very fast. Soon water covered the island, and the tree floated away.

The tree moved downstream with the current. The river became wider. Other rivers poured into it. The tree passed factories, buildings, and bridges. Ships went by; their waves splashed the tree and rolled it over in the water.

The tree floated out to sea. It moved up and down on the waves. On windy days the waves were so big that the tree

Tree floating past factories and buildings on its way out to sea

would ride to the top of a wave and then glide down the back of it with its roots pointed toward the sky. The waves broke and smashed at the tree and pushed it deep into the water, but it always came up again.

On calm days the tree bobbed gently in the water. Gulls and terns flew over it. Some of the birds landed on the tree and rested. They cleaned their feathers and turned their heads this way and that way as they looked around.

A few weeks later, a bright green seaweed called mermaid's hair started to grow on the tree. Gooseneck barnacles, mussels, oysters, and other animals with shells attached themselves to the tree. Brown seaweed trailed in the water.

Close-up of barnacles

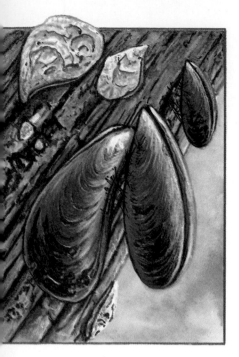

Close-up of oysters and mussels

Sea bass nibbling on seaweed

Small, dark green fish called cunners and young sea bass swam for hours under the tree. They ate the barnacles, oysters, and mussels, and nibbled on the seaweed.

Seawater soaked into the wood, and the wood became darker and softer. The tree was heavier, and it floated deeper in the ocean waters. Almost all spring and summer the tree drifted in the ocean.

Late in the summer a storm blew up. The wind blew very hard, and the waves became larger and larger. Huge waves crashed on a rocky shore.

For two days and two nights the waves battered the tree against the rocks. More branches and roots snapped off. The wood split; chunks of it fell off and drifted away. The rocks smoothed the wood. Almost all the seaweed, barnacles, and oysters were scraped off. After the storm, the tree no longer looked like a tree. It still had a few roots, but it was a battered log rolling in the water.

The log drifted close to shore. Some girls at a beach climbed onto it, and the log became their boat. They took other pieces of wood and paddled with them. Then they pulled the log out of the water and onto the sand.

A very high tide carried the log farther up the beach. A strong wind helped push it along. The log became stuck in the sand.

Waves battering oak tree against rocks

Over the next few months wind blew sand over a part of the log. Slowly the remaining barnacles dried out and fell off. The log began to dry out, and grass roots grew over parts of it.

Beetles crawled on the log. They gnawed little tunnels, through the wood. Then they laid their eggs in the tunnels.

A rat built a nest under the log. It lined the nest with twigs and paper. At night the rat ate grass seeds and hunted on the beach for dead fish and other food. Then the rat scurried back to its nest. It poked its nose out, looked around, and popped back in again.

Beachcombers sawed off parts of the driftwood log for firewood. Sparks popped out of the fires. The flames were

Log on beach

colored blue, green, and orange by the dry sea salts in the old wood. People enjoyed watching the flames at night.

Part of a root remained on the log. The root was gnarled and bent. For over a year sand blown by the wind had rubbed against it and polished it. In the sunlight it shone silvery gray.

One day a boy found the driftwood on the beach. He broke off the root and held it up. He liked its twisted shape and its colors, so he took it home and put it on a shelf in his bedroom. Whenever he looked at it, he thought of the beach. And sometimes he wondered where the driftwood had come from and what had happened to it along the way.

A root of the oak tree

Authors

Louanne Norris and Howard E. Smith, Jr. are a husband-and-wife writing team. Together they have written books for adults and for children. Louanne Norris has been a social worker. Before Howard Smith became a full-time writer, he was a science editor. He also worked on "Mr. Wizard" TV science programs.

A TOAD FOR TUESDAY

**Excerpts from the book
by Russell E. Erickson**

Illustrated by Doug Cushman

In the middle of winter, Warton the toad decided to take some delicious beetle brittle to his Aunt Toolia. His brother, Morton, tried to talk him out of it, but Warton's mind was set. He put on his heaviest sweaters and strapped on his homemade skis. His brother packed some food for him and wished him luck.

On the way, Warton rescued a mouse that was half-buried in the snow. The grateful mouse gave Warton a bright red scarf. If Warton wore the scarf, the mouse said, all of the mouse's relatives would know that the toad was a friend, and they would help him if he ever got into trouble.

The mouse also warned Warton about a dangerous owl who hunted by day, when other owls slept. No sooner had Warton left the mouse than he found himself being chased by this owl. In trying to escape, Warton crashed into a pile of stones, hurting his foot and losing his skis. Suddenly, he was grabbed by strong claws and lifted into the air. The owl carried Warton to his home — a hole near the top of an oak tree. Warton looked around. . . .

It was dark inside and smelled musty. The owl sat the toad in a corner and stepped back. He gave him a piercing look.

"What's your name?" he said.

"Warton."

"Warton?" said the owl. "Well, I think I'll call you . . . Warty."

"I don't care for that very much."

"You don't? Well, that's too bad . . . Warty!"

The little toad got up all his courage and looked right at the owl. "Are . . . are you going to eat me?"

The owl opened his yellow eyes wide. "Am I going to eat you? Of course I'm going to eat you!" Then the owl walked across the room. On the wall a large calendar hung crookedly. The owl pointed at it. "Do you know what this says?"

The toad looked at it closely. "Yes, it says,

BERNIE'S GARAGE
Brakes and Front Ends Our Specialty"

"No! I don't mean that. You're not very bright, are you? It says that in five days it will be next Tuesday. And next Tuesday happens to be my birthday. And finding a little toad in the middle of winter is going to make me a special birthday treat. So, until that day, Warty, you may do as you please. From the looks of your foot I needn't worry about your trying to hop away. Besides, there is no way you can possibly get down from this tree."

The toad looked at his foot. It was twice its normal size. He gave a big sigh. Then he glanced around.

"Tell me, Warty," said the owl, "what do you think of my home?"

Warton looked around again, then he sniffed, then he blinked.

"Well?" said the owl.

"It's terrible," said the toad. "I would certainly hate to live here."

"Don't worry," said the owl, "you aren't going to for long."

"As long as I am here, I would like to make myself comfortable," said Warton. "Do you mind if I light some candles? It seems very dreary in here."

"Dreary?" said the owl. "It seems dreary? Well, go ahead if you want to. It doesn't matter to me."

The toad dug into his pack and pulled out two beeswax candles. As soon as they were lit and began casting their warm glow about the room, he felt much better. He began to straighten his corner. And, being of a cheerful nature, he began to hum a little tune.

The owl couldn't believe his ears. "Warty, you did hear me say that I was going to eat you next Tuesday, didn't you?"

"Yes," said the toad.

The owl shook his head.

Warton continued to busy himself in his corner. Then he turned to the owl and said, "What's your name?"

"I don't know," said the owl. "I guess I don't have one."

"What do your friends call you?"

"I don't have any friends."

"That's too bad," said Warton.

"No, it isn't too bad," snapped the owl. "Because I don't want any friends and I don't need any friends. Now, be quiet!"

Warton nodded. After a while he said, "If you did have a name, what would you like it to be?"

The owl began to be a little flustered. He wasn't used to talking to anyone, especially in his home. "Well, if I had a name . . ." he said slowly, "if I had a name . . . if I had a name . . . I think I would like . . . George."

"Uh huh," said the toad. He went back to straightening his corner.

The owl was becoming sleepy. He fluffed his feathers and closed his eyes.

Just as he was beginning to doze off, the toad called, "Hey, George!"

The owl's eyes popped open. "Are you talking to me?"

"Yes," said the toad. "Do you mind if I make some tea?"

"Oh, go ahead," said the flabbergasted owl.

Warton took some more things out of his pack and prepared the tea. Shortly, he had a steaming pot of refreshing tea.

"It's ready, George," said the toad.

"What's ready?" growled the sleepy owl.

"Our tea."

"I don't want any."

"But I've already got it poured," said Warton.

"Oh, all right," grumbled the owl.

Then, by the light of the beeswax candles, the owl and the toad sat down to tea.

The owl talked and the toad listened. Then the toad talked and the owl listened. It wasn't until the latest hours of that night when the owl finally said, "I'm too tired to talk any more." And he went to sleep.

Warton put away the teacups and then he put out the beeswax candles. As he lay in the still darkness he tried very hard to think of what he should do. But, because of the very busy day he had had and because of all the new experiences, his tired head just would not work at all. He was soon snoring softly.

When the toad awoke the next morning, the owl was gone. The swelling on Warton's foot had gone down but it was still quite sore. The sun shone in through the doorway, and in the bright light of day the owl's home did not seem nearly as gloomy as it had the night before. But it did look every bit as cluttered.

Warton poked through his pack trying to find something that would be just right for breakfast. He selected an ant-egg salad sandwich. As he unwrapped it his eyes turned to the wall opposite the doorway. A ray of sunlight fell directly on the owl's calendar. A large circle had been drawn around the day of his birthday, and an X put upon the day just past.

Only five days were left!

Warton's appetite nearly vanished, but he managed to eat his breakfast. When he was finished he went to the doorway and looked out.

The snow-covered ground was far, far below, and there was not a branch anywhere near that he could jump to.

And even if he did somehow get down from the tree his foot was still too sore to travel on. "I shall just have to wait a bit," he thought.

All this time Warton had been studying the owl's home. Now something was bothering him almost as much as the coming of next Tuesday. That was the sorry state of the owl's housekeeping. Warton could stand it no longer. Immediately he set about cleaning up the mess.

All morning and all afternoon he cleaned. He didn't even stop for lunch. He had barely finished his work when he heard the soft flapping of wings.

The owl had returned a little earlier than usual. He had never thought of cleaning his home himself, so he was astonished at what he saw.

"It doesn't look too bad, Warty," he said. Then he puffed himself up, and his eyes opened wide. "But don't think I'm going to change my mind about next Tuesday."

"I didn't do it for that reason," said Warton. He went to his pack and took out a fresh washcloth. Then he washed off all the dirt and dust that had gotten on him during the day.

When he was done he unwrapped another of the sandwiches Morton had made for him, and quietly ate his supper.

All the while he was eating his sandwich the owl stared straight at him. And all the while he ate his dessert, the owl stared straight at him.

When Warton swallowed the very last bite the owl said, "Are you going to make tea again tonight?"

"Perhaps I will," said Warton.

"Perhaps I will have some too," said the owl softly.

So that night the toad and the owl once again sat down to tea. And once again it was very late before they slept.

The following morning, when the toad awoke, the owl was gone as before. Warton's foot felt much better, so the first thing he did was to look at the calendar. "Only four more days — I must do something soon," he thought anxiously.

He went to the doorway and looked down — it was still just as far to the bottom of the tree.

He tried calling to a sparrow, then a chickadee, then a nuthatch, but all the little birds knew the owl lived in that tree. None would come near.

Warton hopped all about, looking for some means of escape. He came upon a few of the owl's last year's feathers that he had somehow missed when he cleaned the owl's home.

"Maybe if I tie some of the feathers to my arms, I could glide to the ground," he thought. Then he laughed aloud at the silliness of the idea.

He decided to clean the owl's home again. When there was nothing left to clean, he ate his lunch. Then he did some jumping exercises to clear his head for serious thinking. When his head was clear, he squatted under the kitchen table and began to think.

First one eye blinked, then the other. Slowly, at first, then faster and faster he blinked, until everything became a blur. Then he stopped, smiling.

He hopped to the doorway again and looked down. "I think two and a half will do it," he said, hopping back to his corner. Opening his pack, he took out his three tightly-knitted sweaters. The blue one, the yellow one, and the white one with the red reindeer.

"There is more than enough strong yarn here to reach the bottom of this tree," he thought.

He began unraveling the blue sweater. And as he unraveled, he tied small loops in the yarn, just far enough apart for him to step into.

"This ladder is going to take me a couple of days," he thought, looking anxiously at the calendar. "And of course, I won't be so warm, and I won't have my skis, but at least I'll be free."

For the rest of the day he unraveled and made loops and hummed softly. When he thought it was almost time for the owl to come home he hid everything in his pack.

It was none too soon, for the owl had returned even earlier than the day before. After supper the two had tea.

Drinking tea always put Warton into a mood for talking. And now that he knew he had a way of escaping he felt relaxed. Over their second cup of tea, he told the owl about the time he and Morton had come home from blueberry picking and found two snakes sleeping on their doorstep. He told how they had tied the snakes' tails together, hit them on their noses with the blueberry pails, then hopped off in different directions. When the snakes tried to catch them they became so snarled that Warton and Morton were able to roll them down the hill like a big ball, straight into the home of a cranky skunk.

The toad chuckled as he told the story. Then he noticed that the owl was laughing. "I'm glad you liked the story," said Warton.

"I didn't say that I liked it," snapped the owl.

"But you were laughing," said the toad.

"I was?" said the owl. "I don't believe I ever did that before."

As the toad filled their cups again, the owl said, "This is very good tea."

"Yes, it is," said Warton, "but not as good as my favorite of all teas."

"What is that?" asked the owl.

"Juniper-berry tea. My cousin once brought me some. I've never tasted any as good. But it grows only in certain places and I've never had it again."

And they talked some more.

After Warton blew out the beeswax candles he said, "Goodnight, George."

There was a long, long silence. Then the owl said, "Goodnight, Warty."

The next day was just the same. In the morning when the toad awoke, the owl was gone. Warton worked on his unraveled-sweater-ladder until the owl returned. Later they drank some tea and had a chat.

On Sunday morning, even though his ladder wasn't finished, Warton decided to test it.

He fastened one end to the owl's saggy sofa. The other end he dropped out of the doorway. Lying on his belly, he placed one foot over the edge and into the first loop. That one held.

He put his other foot into the next loop. That one held, too. Now he could see all the way to the ground, and it made him dizzy.

But Warton had to be sure that his ladder would really work. So down he went to another loop, another, and then another. Finally he was satisfied.

Climbing back up was much more difficult. Warton was all out of breath when he crawled into the owl's home. After a few minutes' rest he went back to work on his ladder. From time to time he glanced anxiously at George's clock. Because it had only the small hand it was very difficult to know exactly what time it was.

Finally, even though he had much more to do, Warton dared not work any longer. "Tomorrow I will have to work as fast as I can every possible minute if I am to finish in time," he thought. As he put the ladder in his pack another thought came to him, "Unless . . . unless George changes his mind. Then I won't need this ladder at all." Warton was thinking about how the owl came home earlier and earlier each day and how he seemed to enjoy their chats very much. At times he even seemed almost friendly. "Why, he may not eat me after all!" The thought suddenly made Warton feel quite happy.

But that day the owl returned home later than he had ever done before. It was almost dark when he stepped through the doorway.

Warton was still feeling quite happy. "Good evening, George," he said cheerily. "Did you have a nice day today?"

The owl stood staring down at the toad, his eyes cold as ice. "No . . ." he said slowly, "I did not have a nice day. I have been crunched up in a hollow log since early this morning. I did not catch the mouse that I chased in there, and when I started to come out, a fox was waiting at the entrance. He didn't leave until a short while ago. I have had nothing to eat all day. I am hungry and I am stiff and a storm must be coming because my talons are beginning to ache terribly."

Warton's happiness vanished instantly. He knew now that to depend upon the owl's having a change of heart could be a fatal mistake. The ladder was his only hope, and yet there was so much more work to do and — the toad sighed — so little time.

Then the worst thing happened: The owl discovered Warton's ladder and threw it away. He was very angry and wouldn't speak to the toad all that evening or the next evening. Then, the next morning, on Warton's last day, the owl left as usual. Soon after, the toad heard a strange scratching sound that kept getting louder and louder. A hole suddenly appeared in the wall, and a mouse climbed into the room. He said his name was Sy. He had seen Warton's red scarf, and he and his family had decided to rescue the toad. Warton quickly packed and followed Sy through a tunnel that led outside. There he saw one hundred mice on skis. The mice had made them after seeing Warton ski. Forming two lines, Warton and the mice set out for Aunt Toolia's.

After a while, they stopped to rest in an open meadow, where something caught Warton's eye.

Down below, near the stream, some kind of a struggle was going on. Puffs of snow flew in every direction. Even from such a distance, a great deal of screeching and growling could be heard. When the snow cleared away for an instant, Warton saw someone he thought he knew.

"George?" he said under his breath. Shading his eyes from the bright sun, he looked again.

He was right. George the owl was struggling frantically to free himself from the jaws of a snarling fox. Warton could see at once that George didn't have the slimmest chance. Even now, the owl's wings were flapping weakly against the snow, while flying feathers filled the air.

Warton hopped to his feet and strapped on his skis.

"Where are you going?" asked Sy.

"I'm going to help George."

"George? Who's George?"

"George, the owl," said Warton.

"But . . . but . . . I thought we were helping you to get away from him," said Sy in bewilderment.

"Yes," said Warton, "but I just can't stand here and watch that fox eat him."

"But, he was going to eat *you*."

Warton wasn't listening. He pushed off toward the icy stream.

Sy scratched his head. "I never did understand toads. Well, come on, my brothers!" he squeaked with a twitch of his whiskers, "Let's give him a hand."

At once, all the mice jumped onto their skis and pushed off after Warton. The sunny hillside was one great wave of skiing mice as they flashed over the glistening snow. A powdery cloud rose high behind them as the one hundred mice and one toad swept downwards.

The fox looked up and blinked unbelievingly. Faster and faster they came, the sharp points of their poles glittering like diamonds and each one pointing straight at him. Quickly the fox decided that he wanted no part of whatever it was.

He released the owl, and bounded off through the deep snow as fast as his shaking legs would go.

The toad was the first to reach the owl. Most of the mice stopped a safe distance away, but Sy and a few of his brothers kept right after the terrified fox.

Warton looked sideways at the crumpled owl. Feathers were scattered all over the snow. Some floated slowly away in the icy stream. The owl's wings were badly tattered and one of his big yellow eyes was swollen completely shut.

As he looked at the once proud bird, Warton felt sad.

"Hello, Warty," said the owl weakly.

"Hello, George," said the toad.

"What are you doing here?" asked the owl.

"I'm escaping."

The owl's one good eye opened wide. "Escaping? Escaping from what?" he said, clearly annoyed.

"From you," said the toad. "Today is your birthday, and you said you were going to eat me. I was to be your special treat."

The owl started to shake his head, but it hurt too much. "Didn't you see my note?" he said, sounding more and more exasperated.

"I — I didn't have time."

"Well, if you had, you would have known that I was coming home soon, and that I was going to bring a surprise."

"A surprise?" said Warton.

"That's what I said. I first came here to the stream to get a nice fish for supper, which I did. But, the surprise is over there, and that's where the fox caught me." The owl turned and pointed to some bluish-green bushes.

"Why, those are juniper bushes," said the toad.

"That's right," said the owl. "You said juniper berries made your favorite kind of tea, didn't you?"

Warton hardly knew what to say. "But I don't understand . . . do you mean you came here to pick them for me, and you weren't going to eat me, ever?"

"Of course I was going to eat you — until last night, that is." The owl spoke more softly. "Because we weren't speaking, I thought quite a bit last night.

I thought about our chats and other things, and I thought that perhaps having a friend might not be too bad. I mean . . . I don't need any friends, of course . . . but . . ." As he spoke, two feathers fluttered to his feet. Then the owl turned his head so that Warton couldn't look at him. When he spoke again his voice was so soft the toad could barely hear him. "But if I ever do have a friend . . . I hope he is just like you . . . Warton."

Warton was stunned. From somewhere deep inside, a small lump had come into his throat. "Do you mean you would like us to be friends?" he said.

The owl nodded his head.

Then the toad hopped around to where he could look up at him. "I would be happy to be your friend, George."

The owl looked down and a big smile slowly spread across his battered face. "Well, that's fine. That's just fine. I'm so happy I promise I'll never eat another toad again." He looked around at Sy and his brothers, "Or a mouse, for that matter."

The mice cheered.

"Now, if I can still fly," he said, shaking out a few more loose feathers, "I'd be glad to take you the rest of the way to your Aunt Toolia's."

The toad hopped onto his back, shouting good-bye and thank you to Sy and to all his brothers. It took the owl some time to lift out of the snow, but finally he rose into the air.

The higher he flew, the stronger he became. Warton waved to the mice as, far below, they grew smaller and smaller. Then the forest trees seemed to float beneath them as they made a great circle in the blue sky and turned towards Aunt Toolia's.

Author

A Toad for Tuesday is the first book Russell Erickson wrote about the two toad brothers, Warton and Morton. This book was honored by the American Library Association as a Notable Children's Book, and it was chosen as an outstanding book by the Child Study Association. Mr. Erickson went on to write more adventures of the funny pair, including *Warton and Morton*, and *Warton and the Castaways*.

WARTON AND
THE KING
OF THE SKIES

BY RUSSELL E. ERICKSON

PICTURES BY LAWRENCE DI FIORI

Houghton Mifflin Literature

You have read several stories about journeys. One story was about a toad named Warton. Russell Erickson, the author of *A Toad for Tuesday* tells more of Warton the toad's adventures in *Warton and the King of the Sky*. In this story, Warton goes on another journey . . . and yes, Warton gets into a tight spot again!

6

Learning Lessons

Hannah is a Palindrome
by Mindy Warshaw Skolsky

Photographs by Ralph Mercer

There were two things in school Hannah had never been picked to be. The first was monitor when the teacher had to leave the room. The second was the person who clapped erasers together to clean the chalk dust out. "I wonder if Miss Pepper knows about that," thought Hannah.

So one morning she wrote a note in school, and it said:

Dear Miss Pepper,
Did you know that I was never monitor and also I never clapped erasers?
I wish I could do one or two of those things.
Because I am going to be a teacher.
Best of all, I'd like to be monitor.

Love, Hannah

P.S. *But I also like to clap erasers.*

Then she went up to the pencil sharpener and sharpened her pencil. On the way back to her seat, she dropped the note on Miss Pepper's desk.

Miss Pepper cleared her throat. She opened the drawer at the top of her desk and took out a little box. Hannah looked to see if it said "Cherry" or "Licorice." All day long Miss Pepper sucked on cherry or licorice cough drops. "I have a dry throat," she always said. Hannah loved cherry *and* licorice cough drops. She could never decide which she liked better. When somebody was monitor, if they kept the room quiet, Miss Pepper would say, "Well done," when she got back. And then she would say, "Would you like a cherry or a licorice cough drop?" All the kids liked cough drops. But no one except Miss Pepper or a good monitor could eat them in school without a note from a doctor.

Hannah dreamed of being monitor and being offered cherry or licorice, but in her dream she could never decide which. Sometimes Hannah still had trouble making up her mind. But she didn't want Miss Pepper to know that, because Miss Pepper had a rule, "Don't be indecisive." Hannah had looked up "indecisive" in the dictionary, and she decided that rule meant "Make up your mind."

The box said "Cherry," and Hannah licked her lips as Miss Pepper popped the cherry cough drop into her mouth.

Hannah said "mmm" to herself, but she didn't say it out loud. Miss Pepper had a lot of rules of good behavior in the classroom, and "Don't say 'mmm'" was one of them. In school, Hannah always tried to control herself and follow all Miss Pepper's rules of good behavior. At home, she acted natural.

Miss Pepper stood up.

"It is time for our new word of the day," she said. "It's a big one." Miss Pepper loved big words.

Otto Zimmer groaned.

Miss Pepper sucked on her cough drop and looked at Otto.

"Otto," she said, "you know the rules of good behavior in this class. And 'No groaning' is one of them."

Miss Pepper gave a new word every day. She had a special place on the blackboard to write it. She always wrote the new word in the special place and then she asked someone to look it up in the dictionary. Then that person had to tell the definition. Then everybody wrote it five times. And then they took it home for homework and wrote it five more times and made up a sentence with the new word in it.

All the children liked to be picked to be monitor or clap erasers. But nobody liked to be picked to look up words in the dictionary. Looking up words in the dictionary was hard. Miss Pepper's dictionary was fat and it was on a special dictionary stand in the corner. It was hard to make it stay open to the page you wanted. There was so much little print on each page, and it was easy to lose your place while you were looking back at the special place on the blackboard to see the word. If you lost your place, the pages flopped over and you had to start all over again. Once that had happened to Aggie Branagan three times in a row, and Aggie had burst into tears. Hannah had never been picked to be monitor or clap erasers. But Miss Pepper often called on her to look up new words. Hannah hated it, like playing scales on the piano.

"Today's word is a really hard one," said Miss Pepper. "Three syllables!" Hannah started to slump down in her seat so Miss Pepper wouldn't see her and call on her. But then she remembered the rule "Watch your posture; don't be a slumper," so she sat up tall.

Miss Pepper went to the blackboard. She picked up a piece of chalk. Under the place where it said "Word of the Day," she wrote *palindrome*.

"Who would like to look this word up in the dictionary?" asked Miss Pepper.

Everybody looked at the floor except some kids who looked at the ceiling. Aggie made believe she had dropped something and hid her head under her desk.

Miss Pepper looked around the room. "I'll give you a hint," she said. She looked at Hannah.

"Oh, no!" said Hannah to herself. "Not again!"

Under the word, Miss Pepper wrote, "Hannah is a palindrome."

Hannah was very surprised. She had never seen herself in a sentence before.

"What's a palindrome?" she wondered.

Miss Pepper raised her chalk to write again.

Just then the buzzer rang. That meant Miss Pepper had to leave the room.

"Who would like to be the monitor while I am gone?" she asked.

All the children raised their hands.

Hannah waved her hand round and round in the air. She wiggled a lot in her seat even though "Don't wiggle" was one of the rules of good behavior. But she wanted to be monitor so much. She also wanted to win a cherry or a licorice cough drop even though she couldn't decide which.

"Hannah," said Miss Pepper, "You have always been a conscientious student who follows the rules except for sometimes when you get the giggles. Being monitor is serious business. It means being the teacher when the teacher is away. If you're sure you wouldn't get the giggles, there is no reason why you shouldn't get a chance to be monitor." She looked at Hannah's note and added, "Also, it would be good practice for you."

Hannah almost flew into Miss Pepper's big chair in front of Miss Pepper's big desk.

"Now I know everyone will be quiet and do his or her word work till I get back," said Miss Pepper. "But if anyone breaks a rule of good behavior, Hannah, just write his or her name down on the blackboard."

Miss Pepper always said that.

The monitor always wrote names down on the blackboard. Besides wanting to feel like a teacher and get a cough drop, that was one of the reasons Hannah wanted to be monitor so much. Before her grandmother had moved back to New York City, she had bought Hannah a blackboard. Hannah used to write her grandmother's name down when her grandmother talked. But that was just one name. And now she didn't even get to do that. So now Hannah wanted to be a real monitor in real school and write down a lot of real names. "I'll have fun," she thought.

"Remember all the rules of good behavior while I am gone," said Miss Pepper to the class. "Control yourselves. Do your word work. And act like little ladies and gentlemen. Hannah is your monitor."

Then she left the room.

As soon as the door closed, Otto made a rude noise. Otto always made rude noises when Miss Pepper left the room.

"Stop that, Otto," said Hannah. "You know the rules of good behavior in this classroom."

"Hannah is a palindrome!" said Otto.

"Oh, I am not," Hannah wanted to say. But it was written right on the blackboard.

Hannah wondered what a palindrome was. She didn't want Otto to know she didn't know.

"No talking out, Otto!" said Hannah. "That's one of the rules and you know it. Who will look up today's word in the dictionary?"

"Raspberries!" said Otto.

"Otto!" said Hannah. "I'm warning you. I *mean* it, Otto."

Otto just made more raspberry noises.

"I'm serious, Otto," said Hannah. "I'll give you one more chance."

"Hannah is a palindrome!" said Otto.

"That's enough fooling around, Otto," said Hannah. "I gave you two chances already."

She picked up a piece of chalk and wrote "Otto Zimmer" on the blackboard. She wrote with her best penmanship because "Don't write with poor penmanship" was another one of Miss Pepper's rules. While Hannah was writing, the chalk squeaked.

"Eek!" said Otto, imitating the chalk.

"You want me to write your name down twice?" asked Hannah.

"Hannah is a palindrome!" said Otto.

"Otto! *No talking!*" said Hannah. "That's the most important rule!"

All Miss Pepper's rules were important, like "No getting the giggles, because you could pass it on to your neighbor," and "Never waste paper on a paper airplane, and if you do don't sail it." But some rules were more important than others.

"No talking" was the most important rule of all.

All of a sudden other kids were talking too.

"No talking!" said Hannah to the class. "I *mean* it. Now who is going to look up that word?"

But the kids who were talking kept right on talking.

"I'll give you one more chance," said Hannah.

But they kept right on talking.

"Hannah is a palindrome!" said Willie Hoffman.

Frankie Canelli and Eddie Bugbee said it right after him.

So Hannah wrote,

WILLIE HOFFMAN
FRANKIE CANELLI
EDDIE BUGBEE

under "Otto Zimmer."

Then Alfred Hennessy made a little paper airplane and sailed it across the room at Philip Higgle.

"No paper airplanes, Alfred," said Hannah. "Now who is going to look up that word?"

Philip Higgle sailed the little paper airplane back at Alfred Hennessy.

"Listen, Alfred and Philip," said Hannah, "I *mean* it. Stop sailing little airplanes."

So they made and sailed medium-sized ones instead.

Hannah wrote,

ALFRED HENNESSY
PHILIP HIGGLE

underneath

OTTO ZIMMER
WILLIE HOFFMAN
FRANKIE CANELLI
EDDIE BUGBEE

She tried to have good penmanship and have straight margins, because "Don't forget your margins" was in the rules too. While she was writing, an airplane landed on her shoulder. Hannah whirled around.

"Who made that airplane?" she asked.

Nobody answered.

Becky Jackson started to giggle. Aggie Branagan sat across from Becky and Aggie caught the giggles. Hannah usually giggled whenever Aggie did, but today Hannah didn't giggle. She just said, "Aggie!" and stared at her. "You're my *friend,*" she tried to say with her eyes.

Aggie's face got very red. She said, "I'm sorry, but I can't help it, Hannah. You looked so funny with that airplane on your shoulder!" She put her hands over her mouth, but she didn't stop giggling. Becky giggled with her.

Hannah sighed. She knew she couldn't play favorites. So she wrote,

BECKY JACKSON
AGGIE BRANAGAN

Then she turned around and said, "Who is going to look up that word?"

Nobody answered.

They all started to talk, giggle, and sail airplanes instead.

It looked like a roomful of big white birds swooping and dipping all around Hannah's head.

One big airplane even sailed out the window.

Hannah clapped her hands together loudly, as Miss Pepper did when the room got too noisy. She even said, "This is disgraceful behavior!" the way Miss Pepper did, but no one heard her. They were too busy talking, giggling, and making and sailing paper airplanes. Hannah didn't feel one bit like giggling. She felt like putting her hat on her head, walking out of the room, and going home. But there was another rule, "Don't give up the ship." It meant "Keep trying."

So Hannah didn't give up the ship. She wanted Miss Pepper to say, "Well done," when she came back into the room, like she did to the other good monitors.

"Hannah is a palindrome!" yelled Otto.

Then everybody in the room said it with him — except Aggie. Aggie wasn't giggling anymore. But her face was still red.

Hannah wrote,

SUSAN SLOTNICK
MARTHA CARLSON
MARTIN MARKOWITZ
JOE ROBERTS
ALLEN GREEN
ROBERTA BLEIGLE
JOANN HIGGINS
ELMER JONES
JENNY RICHARDS
TESSIE SIMON
MELBA PRINGLE

Hannah's right arm was getting tired. Her penmanship was getting harder to read. Her margins weren't so straight anymore. "I don't like being monitor so much," she thought. She wished Miss Pepper would hurry up and come back and say, "This is disgraceful behavior!" to the rest of the class and "Well done, Hannah." Besides, there wasn't any more room on the blackboard to write more names. Also, there weren't any names left to write. Hannah had written the name of every kid in the class. But it was no fun.

"They'll really get it when Miss Pepper comes back," she thought. "Wait — maybe *I'll* get it. Maybe Miss Pepper will say, 'Why didn't you keep them quiet?' Maybe I won't get a cherry *or* a licorice cough drop."

"Who is going to look up that word?" said Hannah one more time. But she knew no one would answer. They were too busy yelling, "Hannah is a palindrome." Except Aggie. Aggie was sitting up tall now with her hands folded on her desk. She looked like she was going to cry. Hannah was sorry she had written Aggie's name on the blackboard and wished there was some way she could take it off without playing favorites.

An eraser sailed through the air. "No throwing erasers!" said Hannah. "That's a rule!"

The biggest airplane of all sailed by. It said HANNAH IS A PALINDROME in great big capital letters that Hannah could read as it sailed by.

Everybody laughed except Hannah and Aggie. Hannah felt like crying, but she had one rule of her own: "Never cry in front of other kids."

"This is terrible," she said to herself. "How will I ever be a teacher? No one is even listening to me. I can't decide what to do."

All the kids except Aggie were up out of their seats sailing airplanes and throwing erasers. Aggie had her head hidden underneath her desk again.

Hannah walked over to the dictionary. No one even noticed her.

She looked up "palindrome." She read for a long time. More erasers and airplanes sailed by. Hannah ignored them.

After she had finished looking in the dictionary, she looked at Otto. She closed the dictionary and picked it up. It was very heavy.

Hannah carried it to Miss Pepper's desk.

"Quiet!" she said. "I looked up the word myself. I'm *telling* you something!"

THUMP! An eraser bounced off Hannah's head.

Hannah forgot about the rule "Control yourself."

She slammed the big heavy dictionary down on Miss Pepper's desk. She slammed it down so hard she thought the desk would break in half. It made such a loud bang, even Hannah jumped. Aggie screamed. Otto's lower jaw flopped open.

And the room got quiet. The erasers stopped. The airplanes stopped. The kids sat down and stared at Hannah.

She picked up all the airplanes. She picked up all the erasers. She erased all the names so she would have room to write.

She picked up a new piece of chalk. Underneath where Miss Pepper had written the new word and the sentence, Hannah wrote, "Otto is a palindrome."

She wrote slowly and carefully. The chalk didn't squeak.

Otto's mouth fell open even wider.

Hannah turned around and faced the class.

"A palindrome," she said, "is a word that is spelled the same backward as forward. Now write it five times and for homework use it in a sentence."

The room was very quiet.

The door opened and Miss Pepper walked in.

Miss Pepper looked all around.

"Why, what a lovely class," she said. "How nice it makes me feel to think you were so well behaved and quiet while I was gone. Not one name on the blackboard. And 'Otto is a palindrome'! Why, I was just about to write that on the blackboard myself when the buzzer rang. How clever of you to figure that out by yourself, Hannah. What a good teacher you are. Well done, Hannah. Would you like a licorice or a cherry cough drop?"

Hannah couldn't answer. All of a sudden she felt very tired. She went back to her seat and sat down. She put her head down on top of her desk. Inside the circle of her arms, she did some thinking. "What should I tell her?" she wondered. She was ashamed to accept a cough drop. Also, she still hadn't decided which flavor.

So she took out a piece of paper and wrote Miss Pepper another note. She wrote:

Dear Miss Pepper,

It wasn't really quiet while you were gone.

People talked and yelled and threw erasers and sailed airplanes.

I clapped my hands and stamped my feet and wrote all the names on the blackboard. There wasn't any more room to write so I had to erase.

Nobody would look up palindrome in the dictionary. So I looked up palindrome in the dictionary. That's how I figured out about Otto.

I didn't giggle. But I slammed the dictionary down on your desk.

It made a big bang.

Everybody jumped. I jumped too. And that's how it finally got quiet.

It got quiet just before you came in the door.

I was a terrible monitor. I'll never be able to be a teacher.

Love,
Hannah

P.S. *Do I still get the cough drop?*

Hannah went up to the pencil sharpener again and sharpened her pencil till there was nothing left but a point on one end and an eraser on the other. She dropped the note on Miss Pepper's desk on her way back to her seat.

Miss Pepper read the note.

When she finished, she said, "Well, of all things! Hannah, this sounds just like a description of what happened to me on the very first day of the very first year I was a teacher! I know exactly how that feels. I slammed a book down like that myself! That's when I started to make Miss Pepper's Rules and Regulations of Good Behavior. Now if there's one thing I like it's an honest person! You used your ingenuity — and that will be the new word for tomorrow. All right, Otto, stop that groaning. Would you like to clap the erasers together now, Hannah? And would you like a cherry or a licorice cough drop?"

Hannah stared at Miss Pepper. She had never heard her teacher say things like that before. She couldn't believe it — Miss Pepper talked like a real person!

After a while, Hannah got up. She took the erasers over to the window. She opened a window and clapped erasers together two at a time. Clouds of chalk dust went up in the air. Hannah coughed. She looked up and watched the chalk clouds float up toward the real clouds. The sky was bright, blue, and beautiful.

When all the chalk dust was gone, Hannah closed the windows. She put the erasers back. She went over to Miss Pepper's desk.

She looked at the little box that said "Licorice" and she looked at the little box that said "Cherry."

"I made a decision," said Hannah. "I'll have one of each, please."

Back at her desk, Hannah wrote one last note:

Dear Aggie,

Come to The Grand View Restaurant after we go home. We'll have an ice-cream cone and play school. And I'll give you one lick of each cough drop.

Love from your friend,
Hannah

P.S. *I'll be the teacher, of course.*

Author

Mindy Warshaw Skolsky began writing stories for her students when she was a teacher. She has continued to write them for her own children. Mrs. Skolsky sees writing as a lovely opportunity to tell stories to children. There are several books about Hannah and her adventures.

Moose
Baby

by Berniece Freschet

Illustrated by Jeremy Guitar

AT THE MARSH

It was May. The morning sun shone bright, and the air smelled sweet.

Hidden in the tall marsh grasses, a wild goose sat on a nest of eggs. Close by, a gander stood guard, his long neck held high.

At the edge of the marsh, a moose lifted her head out of the water. Long ribbons of water weeds hung down from her ears.

The big moose came out of the water. She moved slowly. It was almost time for her calf to be born.

She looked for a grassy place to lie down. She came to some willow bushes where she could hide. Here, her baby was born.

The mother moose licked her newborn baby clean.

In a little while the small calf tried to get up. But his legs were weak. When he got his front legs up, his back legs fell. And when he got his back legs up, his front legs gave out.

The little moose tried again. Finally, weak and wobbly, Moose Baby stood, his long stick-legs spread wide. It felt strange. His body shook. First he swayed forward, and then he swayed backward.

Moose Baby tried to take a step, but his legs slipped out from under him. He sat down hard.

The mother moose knew her calf needed milk to grow strong. She gave him a gentle push. Moose Baby struggled to his feet. This time he found his mother's warm milk.

After he drank, he could stand without swaying. Moose Baby took three, and even four, steps before he fell.

He lay down on the soft bed of grasses. The mother moose stood close. She put out her wet, rough tongue and licked her funny-looking little calf with the big nose.

SKUNKS DON'T PLAY FAIR

Moose Baby had big feet, a big head, and a great big nose. His long upper lip hung down, and he was awkward.

When he ran fast, his long stick-legs got in his way and he would trip and fall.

His reddish-brown fur coat was much lighter than his mother's. And he did not have a hump on his shoulders, like his mother, or the "bell" of whiskers that hung under her chin. When he was older, he would grow them.

Early one morning, Moose Baby stood by the marsh. He watched his mother duck her head under the water. She was looking for plant roots to eat. She liked the tender water lilies the best of all.

Moose Baby felt like playing. He jumped over a rock. He looked for someone to play with. He saw small fish swimming near. He waded into the water, but the fish swam away.

A beaver swam to the bank. He pushed out of the water and waddled up to a tree. With his sharp, orange teeth, the beaver chewed on the tree. Wood tree chips flew into the air.

Maybe the beaver liked to play? Moose Baby came close. But the beaver did not even lift his head. He kept right on chewing. He was cutting down trees for the dam he must build. The busy beaver had no time for Moose Baby.

A small brown mouse popped out of a hole. She stopped to eat weed seeds.

Moose Baby moved near. He put his head down for a close look. He sniffed. The mouse ran and hid under a bush.

Moose Baby moved on.

He came to a family of skunks. The mother skunk was digging under a log. She knew that fat bugs were under the log.

The baby skunks began to dig too.

Moose Baby moved near. The mother skunk was afraid for her babies. Was this huge beast an enemy? She raised her tail high. She beat her feet on the ground, warning the moose to go away.

Moose Baby did not know about the warning. He came close and then closer. Suddenly his nose was filled with a terrible smell. The smell was so bad that he ran and splashed into the marsh waters. He stayed in the water for a very long time. Now Moose Baby knew.

Skunks do not make good playmates.

THE COYOTE

One moonlit night Moose Baby heard a strange, wild sound. It was a coyote howling at the moon.

Moose Baby was afraid. Maybe he sensed that the coyote was an enemy. Or maybe he felt his mother's fear?

The sky grew light. The howling stopped. But the mother moose was more anxious now.

Moose Baby saw a gray shadow creeping close. He saw yellow eyes and sharp, snarling teeth. Moose Baby was afraid. He ran.

He ran faster than he had ever run before. This time he did not trip and fall. Moose Baby raised his head. WHACK! A tree branch hit him right on his nose. It hurt. He stopped running to look for his mother.

The gray shadow crept close again. With a sudden rush, the coyote ran to attack.

Moose Baby's mother came running. She leaped high. The female moose did not have big antlers like a male moose, but her hoofs were sharp.

She kicked and slashed. There was a yelp of pain. Then all was quiet. The coyote gave up. He ran away to his den in the hills.

But now that the coyote had seen the little moose he would be back. It was no longer safe here.

THE LONG SWIM

Every day the mother moose took her calf for a swim.

Moose Baby liked to swim. Sometimes he saw the wild geese swimming with their goslings. Sometimes he saw the beaver working on his dam. But today, they swam much farther than before.

They were far out into open water. They were swimming in a large lake. They swam toward an island. There the little moose would be safe from the coyote.

Moose Baby was a good swimmer, but it was a long way to the island. After a while he began to tire.

Moose Baby put one of his legs over his mother's back. He rested his head on her neck. When he felt strong again, Moose Baby swam the rest of the way by himself.

Finally they reached the island.

For the first time Moose Baby saw other young calves. Now he had someone to play with. The calves swam and raced together. They bunted bushes with their heads in case an enemy was hiding near.

It was a happy time for the young moose.

On hot afternoons the moose herd lay together in the shade of the trees. When the flies and mosquitoes began to bite, the moose went for a swim, or rolled in the mud. The thick mud helped protect them from the heat, and from the stinging bites of the insects.

The island was a good place for a young moose to learn and grow.

THE MOOSE FIGHT

As the days passed Moose Baby's fur coat grew darker. His hump began to grow. One day the leaves on the trees began to turn red and yellow. It was time for the moose to return to the marsh.

They waded into the water and swam away from the island. This time Moose Baby swam all the way by himself.

As they came to the marsh, Moose Baby heard a loud bellow. A bull moose came crashing out of the woods! He stood over six feet tall. His "bell," the tuft of skin and hair under his neck, was over a foot long.

Huge antlers jutted out from the sides of his head. The scooped antlers curved up into wide platters, called palms, with pointed spikes at the top. These spiked antlers were over six feet wide. The huge bull moose bellowed!

Moose Baby came out of the water. He heard another bellow. A second bull crashed out of the woods. The two giants ran toward each other. Moose Baby stood right in the path of the charging bulls.

Quickly he scrambled out of the way. With a mighty clash of antlers, the two bulls came together.

Moose Baby watched the fight, his heart beating fast. A moose could be badly hurt in a fight such as this. But this fight ended without a winner. From that day on, Moose Baby was careful to stay far away from the fighting bulls.

The air grew colder. Winter was on its way. Cold winds blew, hitting Moose Baby on his face and whistling in his ear. Soon the snow would pile into deep drifts. Food would be hard to find.

The mother moose would teach her youngster how to find food, and how to stay warm through the long, cold winter.

Next spring, small knobs would begin to grow on Moose Baby's head. And when the new calves were born, Moose Baby would be big enough to be on his own.

Author

As Berniece Freschet grew up, she learned to love the outdoors. She has written a number of books, all of them nature stories. She carefully watches each of the animals she writes about. Several of her books have been chosen as outstanding science books: *Bear Mouse, Grizzly Bear, Year on Muskrat Marsh,* and *The Web in the Grass,* a book about spiders.

My Mother Sends Her Wisdom

written by
Louise McClenathan

illustrated by
Rosekrans Hoffman

"Mama," cried Katya, as she peered through the cottage window, "Old Boris, the moneylender, is coming down the road in his horse cart."

"Let him come, little one," answered Katya's mother, as she worked warm dough for bread. The dough made a soft slapping sound against the wooden table.

Boris and Alexei, the small boy who kept his accounts, drew up before the cottage, and the gentle sounds of the house were shattered by the old man's loud pounding on the door. "Widow Petrovna," he shouted, "I have come to collect your monthly rubles due me from the loan of silver to your late husband." His eyes were topaz yellow, like a cat's eyes, and his voice rasped with the sound of greed. Alexei stood with his ledger book and pen, waiting for the rubles to be dropped into his master's soft leather purse.

Mama stood behind Katya, slowly wiping her floury hands on her apron. "Tomorrow, Old Boris," she said, "I shall send you a fine fat goose and gander. My daughter will bring them to your house in the city. Today they would make a clamor in your cart, and the ride would upset the goose's laying. They will be my payment to you this month."

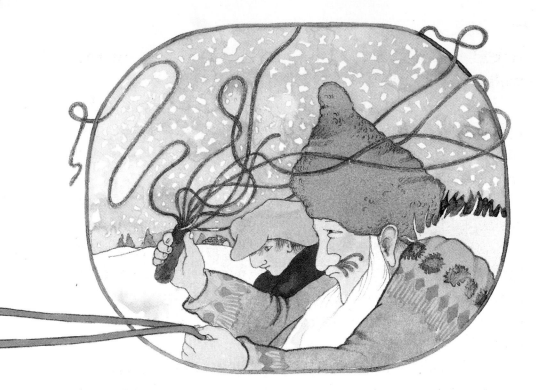

"Very well then, but no later than sundown tomorrow," Boris said.

After his horse and cart disappeared down the road, Mama and Katya sat down for the evening meal. "We shall have one more egg from the good goose, Katya," Mama said cheerfully.

The child ate her soup slowly, thinking about Old Boris. He was hated in the countryside, for he would lend money to the peasant farmers at a very high interest rate and insist on collecting it even if the harvest was poor. When they could not pay, he took over their farms, which he sold to the large landowners.

"Do not worry, Katya," said Mama, as she looked across the table. "I have a plan for Old Boris. If it works, we shall keep our land." While the clock ticked softly and the firelight cast shadows on the walls, Mama told Katya what to do.

They went to sleep bundled in woolens atop the great stove. The heat from the glowing coals warmed the little girl, and she slept easily, knowing that her mother was a wise woman.

The next morning Katya ate her bowl of baked cereal and put on a warm cloak. Mama tucked a small pie filled with meat and onions into her pocket and bade her good-bye. "Remember to repeat to Old Boris everything I told you. Especially to say, 'My mother sends her wisdom.' Do not forget his answer."

With a fat white goose under each arm, Katya set off through the forest. The trees were thick and the woods were silent. She walked quickly, talking to the

goose and gander for company, for it was lonely. There was a smell of snow in the air, and the wind moaned like a wolf crying for the moon.

Soon the forest path grew wider, and she could see spires and roofs of the city houses through the trees. The streets were narrow and crowded. Men pushed carts along, and women cried their wares in the marketplace. "Come buy from me, good bread, good fowl, good brooms today." Katya stumbled along the cobblestones, wishing she were back in the forest again. The city seemed noisy.

An old woman showed her the way to the money-lender's house, which stood on a corner surrounded by a fence. Katya managed to unlatch the gate and lifted the great brass doorknocker. A servant peered out and went to fetch his master. Soon Boris came to the door and opened it wide. Alexei stood behind him. "So you have brought my birds, and high time," snapped the old man.

"Yes, here are the geese for payment, and my mother sends her wisdom," said Katya in a quavering voice.

"Wisdom, is it?" said Old Boris with a laugh.

Katya's eyes were bright as she recited what her mother had taught her:

> "Two well-kept geese, so I've been told,
> May truly lay fine eggs of gold."

Boris shook his head and sneered. "What do I need with the wisdom of a peasant woman?"

"Alexei, mark these geese in the book as payment, then take them to the market to sell."

Katya did not linger and started for home immediately. Without the geese to care for, the journey went quickly.

"And did Old Boris accept my wisdom?" asked Mama, as Katya took off her cloak.

"He laughed, Mama, and said he did not need the wisdom of a peasant woman. Then he ordered the goose and gander sold at the market."

"We shall see, we shall see," murmured Mama, as she warmed the child's feet before the stove.

The next month, on the day payment was due, Katya took two fat pigs through the forest to the moneylender. She kept them moving with her hooked stick, prodding them when they stopped to root in the rich, dark earth.

"Come pig, pig, pig. Come pig, pig, pig," she chanted, and soon they arrived in the city. The sun was high overhead when she reached the moneylender's house. This time Alexei opened the door, and his master shuffled out. "Here are two pigs for payment, and my mother sends her wisdom," said Katya, as the pigs snorted and rooted in the garden.

"What, your mother's wisdom again?" Boris asked scornfully. Katya drew a deep breath and spoke quickly:

"Five pink piglets, born anew,
Will squeal much more than old ones do."

The old man threw back his head and laughed. "If your mother were wise, she would not owe me money. It is the peasant who squeals, not the pig."

Katya did not answer, but turned and quickly went on her way. Soon she was back in the quiet forest, which seemed safer than the noisy, jostling city. When she returned home, she told her mother what Old Boris had answered.

"Good," said Mama, "all is going well, little one."

The festival of Easter was nearing, and together Katya and her mother decorated brightly colored eggs. Some were beet red while others glowed saffron yellow.

Before midnight of Easter eve, the Widow Petrovna and Katya went to pray at church. They lit candles and knelt inside the dark chapel while the stars in the spring night burned in the sky.

The next payment was due on the day after Easter, and Katya woke early that morning. As dawn streaked the Easter Monday sky and the cock crowed, Mama stood by the stove making breakfast.

"Today, Katya, you will take a good sack of wheat to Old Boris," Mama said. "It is heavy, so you must pull it in the little cart and take the dog with you for company."

They loaded the small cart with the wheat, and again Katya set off. She entered the forest with the cart behind her and the dog leaping ahead.

It was cool and the birds sang; bright patches of sunlight filtered through the leaves. The dog chased a rabbit, then returned and tugged at Katya's skirts to hurry her along. "I'm coming, I'm coming," she said with a laugh.

At high noon, she rapped on the moneylender's door and presented the grain. "Here is a sack of wheat for payment, and my mother sends her wisdom."

"What nonsense this time?" asked Old Boris, and Katya recited her mother's riddle:

"How is it that ten grains of wheat
Could give us all enough to eat?"

"I laugh at your mother's wisdom," snapped Old Boris. "She may keep it for herself. Alexei, mark the book for Widow Petrovna and take the wheat to market for sale."

Once more Katya went home and told her mother what the old man had said.

"Now we shall see who is the wiser, daughter," said her mother with a smile, and the two set to work in the garden.

The next month Katya did not visit the money-lender, and one day Old Boris and Alexei came to the cottage and knocked on the door. "You are late with your payment, Widow Petrovna," said the old man. "Do you have nothing to pay this month?"

Mama raised her eyebrows and spoke in a clear voice. "You must be mistaken, Old Boris, for my debt is paid off."

"Paid off, indeed! You still owe twenty rubles, either in money or in goods. Check the book, Alexei."

The boy turned the pages of the heavy book and read the figures. "Twenty rubles still owed, master."

The widow shook her head. "My debt is paid. The sack of wheat was the last payment, and you shall get nothing more. You must go to Judge Petruschka to ask for a hearing against me if you do not believe it, Boris."

"I shall, I shall," said the old man, nodding. "He will find that you are still owing, and I shall be forced to take your land in payment," and he drove off down the road in a cloud of dust.

Soon the day came when Judge Petruschka held court in the district. Old Boris and Alexei sat on one side of the room, while Katya and her mother sat on the other.

"What is the charge?" the judge asked quietly.

"This woman claims she has paid her debt, but she still owes me twenty rubles," said Boris.

"What has she paid you?" the judge asked.

"Two geese, which sold for six rubles. Two pigs, which brought ten rubles at market. A sack of wheat, which sold for four rubles."

"Is this true, Widow Petrovna?" the judge asked.

"No, your honor, it is only half true. My daughter will tell you what she offered Old Boris each time she took payment to him."

Katya stood before the judge and spoke out bravely. "When I took two geese, I offered him my mother's wisdom in this riddle:

'Two well-kept geese, so I've been told,
May truly lay fine eggs of gold.'

"He did not accept my mother's wisdom. If he had, he would have kept the goose and gander, collected many eggs, raised a flock of goslings, and sold them at market for three times what he received."

"When I took the pigs to him, I offered him more of my mother's wisdom in this riddle:

'Five pink piglets, born anew,
Will squeal much more than old ones do.'

"If he had kept the pigs and raised a litter of five piglets, he could have sold them for twice as much as the two pigs brought."

"The third time I offered my mother's wisdom in this riddle:

'How is it that ten grains of wheat
Could give us all enough to eat?'

"He could have sold half the wheat for payment, planted the rest, and had a field of wheat next year, two fields after that, and four the following year."

The judge looked thoughtful. "Is it true, Old Boris, this story the child tells?"

Boris glowered angrily. "Wisdom is not the same as money," he muttered.

The judge sat for a moment, scratching some figures in his book with a long pen. "Such wisdom," he said slowly, "is what feeds us all. I find, Old Boris, that Widow Petrovna has overpaid you some thirty rubles in her wisdom, so it is you who owe her money. I order you to pay her."

The judge would not be moved, though the old man flew into a rage. Finally he drew the money from his purse and flung it on the table.

Katya was trembling, but as she looked at the judge's face she thought she saw a tiny smile hiding around the corners of his mouth.

Soon all the countryside knew that Old Boris had been outdone by the wit of a peasant woman. Friends and relatives came to celebrate, bringing cream from their cows, flowers from their fields, and good strong tea to drink. "We share your joy, Widow Petrovna," they said. "May your land blossom with good fortune always."

Author

Louise McClenathan, who has been called a master storyteller, wrote *My Mother Sends Her Wisdom* in 1979. The idea for the story came from something that happened to a friend's mother. Family traditions or customs interest Ms. McClenathan very much. She has been a reading specialist in Virginia as well as a college planning officer in Pennsylvania. She has written a great many newspaper articles. You might enjoy reading her book *The Easter Pig,* a clever picture-book fantasy with a starry-eyed hero.

Thinking

by Felice Holman

Silently
Inside my head
Behind my eyes
A thought begins to grow and be
A part of me.
And then I think
I always knew
The thing I only got to know,
As though it always
Was right there
Inside my head
Behind my eyes
Where I keep things.

Fables

Houghton Mifflin Literature

There are many kinds of lessons to be learned. You have just read about a few. Now you will read *Fables*, sixteen very short stories by Aesop, Mira Ginsburg, La Fontaine, and Arnold Lobel. Each fable has a moral, or lesson.

7

Clever Ideas

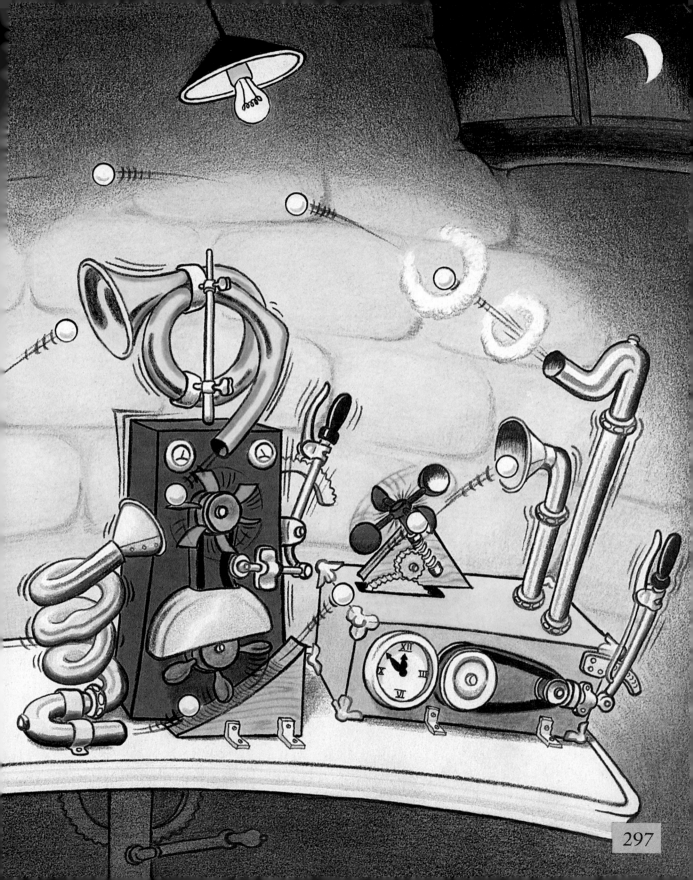

OLD BLUE

by Sibyl Hancock
Illustrated by Eric Ingraham

"Wake up, boy!"

Davy opened his eyes. Cookie was standing over him.

"I'll be right there," Davy said.

He pushed his blanket aside and folded it to make a bedroll. The cowboys sleeping around the campfire would soon wake up hungry for breakfast. And the cowboys riding in from watching the cattle all night would be even hungrier.

A big longhorn steer, with a hide so black it nearly looked blue, lumbered up to Davy and nudged his hand. "Old Blue," Davy said softly. "Are you hungry too?"

Old Blue grunted and shook his widespread horns. Davy laughed. "You think you're better than all those other longhorns. Who ever heard of a big old steer sleeping around the campfire with the cowboys!"

He patted Old Blue's shiny forehead. "You're the smartest old steer I ever saw. Not many ranchers own a steer who can lead all the rest of the cattle on a trail drive."

Davy hurried over to the chuck wagon to help Cookie. He was frying bacon in a black skillet over the fire.

"Pa said I can ride today!" Davy exclaimed.

"Huh! Guess you'll feel like a real big shot!" Cookie said.

Davy smiled. He would be riding up front with the cowboys who guided the longhorn cattle over the trail.

And if Pa said it was okay for him to ride, then it was. Pa was the trail boss.

"You're a lucky boy. Not many young fellows get a chance to go on a trail ride," Cookie told him.

"If Ma hadn't gone to take care of Aunt Clara's new baby, I could never have come," Davy said.

"You can learn plenty on the trail," Cookie said. "But right now there's plenty to do here. Let's get to work!" He handed Davy some tin plates to set out.

"Come and get it!" Cookie yelled.

While the cowboys crowded around the chuck wagon, Davy finished his breakfast. He took a handful of food scraps to Old Blue. The big steer was still eating biscuits and bacon crumbs when Pa brought a horse for Davy to ride.

"Let's get moving," Pa said. "You watch what you're doing up at the front with Old Blue."

"Yes, sir," Davy said.

"Feeling a little shaky?" Pa asked.

Davy nodded.

"I felt the same way on my first trail drive," Pa said. "You'll be fine."

Davy put on his hat. He climbed onto his horse and followed Old Blue up to the head of the herd.

One of the cowboys gave the old Texas call, "Ho, cattle, ho, ho, ho, ho!"

Soon the steers were strung into a line a mile long with Old Blue leading. There were over a thousand of them. Davy watched Old Blue walk steadily to the north.

No one understood how Old Blue knew directions so well. Sometimes Old Blue walked too fast, and the lead cowboys, or point men, had to slow him down.

"I don't like the looks of the sky," one of the cowboys said. "It could be a norther."

Davy shivered. A norther might bring icy weather, and they had a long way to go. They had left the Goodnight ranch in Palo Duro Canyon, Texas, a week ago. It would take two months to bring the herd into Dodge City, Kansas. There the longhorns would be shipped on railroad cars to Chicago.

Davy guided his horse past tumbleweeds rolling slowly in the breeze. Sand crunched under hooves and rose in little gold clouds. Cattle often tried to stop and eat dry clumps of grass. And when they wandered into low mesquite trees, the cowboys had to drive them back to the herd.

Davy looked at the big steer. "Old Blue, you've got your work cut out for you. Here comes the river. We have to get across before the wind changes."

The water was icy, but Old Blue plunged right into it. Cattle and cowboys followed.

"Ho, cattle, ho, ho, ho, ho!" Davy yelled. The cold water splashed onto his face. His horse stumbled, and Davy held on tightly. "Keep going," he said. "Don't fall!" His horse began to swim.

It seemed like a long time before they reached the other side of the river. As the cattle came out of the chilly water, they started running to get warm.

A thousand longhorns pounded the dusty ground.

"Let them run!" Pa shouted. Old Blue would slow them down soon.

By late afternoon the sky grew dark. A streak of lightning flashed. Thunder boomed. There was another sound, too. Horns rattled together, and hooves pounded the dirt.

"Stampede!" Pa cried. "Get out of the way, Davy!" he yelled.

Davy rode his horse away from the frightened steers. He watched the cowboys guide Old Blue around in a circle. The cattle followed. Soon most of the herd were running in a big circle. That was called milling. It was the only way to stop a stampede.

"Whoa, boy!" Davy cried, trying to calm his horse.

The air was full of electricity. Davy could see sparks dancing along the brim of his hat and on the tips of his horse's ears. Pa had called it *foxfire*. It even sparked from horn tip to horn tip over the milling cattle.

As soon as the herd had settled down, Davy rode back to camp. Cookie was at the chuck wagon building a fire.

"Get your slicker on," Cookie said. "It's going to be a bad night."

Davy put on his slicker and ate some cold biscuits and beans. He drank hot coffee to get warm.

"The wind is cold," Davy said.

Pa rode up to the chuck wagon. "We'll need every man in the saddle tonight," he said. "We can't let those longhorns stampede again."

"Do you want me to ride?" Davy asked.

Pa nodded. "I can use your help."

Davy pulled his hat lower over his eyes and rode out with the other cowboys.

Before midnight the rain turned to sleet. Davy could hear someone singing to keep the cattle calm. "Whoop-ee ti yi yo, git along little doggies!" If the longhorns stampeded in this storm, some could get lost and freeze before they were found.

It was the longest night Davy could ever remember. The sleet turned to snow. Davy couldn't even see Old Blue.

By daylight, the worst of the storm was over. The cowboys took turns eating breakfast. Davy stood by the fire trying to get warm.

"You okay, Davy?" Pa asked.

"Just cold," Davy told him.

"Do you want to ride in the wagon with Cookie?" Pa asked him.

Davy shook his head. "No, sir."

"Good boy, Davy. Cookie, how do you ever keep a fire going in all this snow?"

"That's my secret," Cookie said.

"Hey, look who's here," Davy said. Old Blue came close for a bit of Davy's biscuit. "Old Blue, I almost lost you last night," he said, rubbing the steer between his horns. "When we get to Kansas City,

I'm going to buy you a big bell to wear around your neck. Then I'll always know where you are," Davy said. "And so will the cattle."

"Nobody has ever belled a lead steer," Pa said. "But no steer was ever as tame as Old Blue. It's a good idea if it works."

"Davy, you don't have to wait until Kansas City. I've got a bell in the chuck wagon that you can use," Cookie told him. "I'll get it."

He came back with a brass bell and a piece of rope. Davy tied the bell around Old Blue's neck. "There you go, Old Blue. How do you like that?"

Old Blue shook his horns and listened to the bell clang.

"Just look how proud that old steer is," said Pa, laughing.

Davy gave Old Blue a hug. He shook his horns again and rang the bell louder than before. If a longhorn could smile, Old Blue would have.

Author

Sibyl Hancock's book *Old Blue* grew out of her Texas background. She says, "It's great fun to uncover interesting stories that have been almost overlooked by history and turn them into books for children." Old Blue was a real steer in early Texas days, and Mrs. Hancock has seen his horns preserved in a Texas museum.

THE GOLD-TINTED DRAGON

by Karla Kuskin

What's the good of a wagon
Without any dragon
To pull you for mile after mile?
An elegant lean one
A gold-tinted green one
Wearing a dragonly smile.
You'll sweep down the valleys
You'll sail up the hills
Your dragon will shine in the sun
And as you rush by
The people will cry
"I wish that my wagon had one!"

Dragon
Stew

by Tom McGowen

illustrated by Nick Harris

Once upon a time there was a kingdom ruled by a king who was so fat that his people called him King Chubby. He was so fond of food that he couldn't bear to be without it for very long.

Eating was his hobby. He began with a big breakfast at eight o'clock, had a slight snack at ten, and a large lunch at twelve. Then he exercised by watching two tennis players, and since exercise gave him an appetite, he ate a small snack at about two in the afternoon.

At four he had sandwiches and at seven in the evening he happily sat down to a royal banquet. There was one of these every evening, even if the king was the only one at the table.

Eating was so important to him that it affected everything he did. When he fell in love with a duchess from another kingdom, he told her that he would almost rather look at her than eat a whole roast pig. Needless to say, the duchess never spoke to him again.

His love of eating also got him in trouble in other ways. He was always losing his royal cooks. He just couldn't keep from telling them how to improve their cooking. He insisted on making changes in every dish. Since royal cooks are very proud and temperamental, they resented this. Six cooks had already left in a huff.

One evening when the king entered the banquet hall and saw a sandwich on his plate, he knew what had happened.

"Oh, my," he sighed, "I see number seven has left!"

"Yes, your Majesty," replied the major-domo, "he said he could no longer cook for a king who kept changing his recipes. And now there are no more royal cooks available! None of those you've had will ever come back, and all the others are cooking for other kings."

"I don't know how to find another cook. There just aren't any!"

The king looked worried for a moment, then brightened. "I know! A royal cook *is* a royal cook because he has the imagination to make up unusual recipes. There must be many good cooks with imagination in my kingdom. We'll have a contest, and the one who tells me the most unusual recipe can be the royal cook!"

The next day proclamations were posted throughout the kingdom inviting all cooks to enter the contest. There was great excitement. Every housewife who considered herself a good cook and every cook from every inn in the kingdom came clamoring to the castle.

They formed a line which began at the back of the castle, wound around to the front, crossed the drawbridge, entered the gate, jammed the courtyard,

went up the stairs, and flowed into the throne room where the king was interviewing them. In they came, bowing, smiling hopefully, and offering enough recipes to fill seven fat cookbooks or seventy fat kings.

But to each, King Chubby shook his head. "That's not unusual," he'd say, or "I've had that before."

While this was going on, a shabby young man came trudging up the road toward the castle. He had patched knees and elbows, and the feather in his worn hat was bedraggled, but he had a merry grin, and he was whistling a gay tune.

When he saw the long line of people, he asked a soldier, "What's going on?"

"The king's looking for a new royal cook," the soldier replied. "The cook with the most unusual recipe will get the job and will live in the palace off the best of the land!"

"Wouldn't that be wonderful!"

"Well, I don't know," said the soldier. "Cooks don't get along with the king. He tells 'em what to do, puts things in their pots — he all but does the cooking himself."

"You don't say?" said the young man, and he got into line.

"Oh, are you a cook?" asked the soldier.

"I'm just the sort of cook the king wants," he answered, "and I have the most unusual recipe he's ever heard of!"

It was late afternoon when he reached the throne room. The king was looking very glum. Not one cook had offered a recipe he considered unusual. And now the last of them was this ragged fellow who looked far too thin to be much of a cook. "Well, what's your name and recipe?" he asked.

"I'm Klaus Dinkelspiel, your Majesty. My recipe is so unusual, so rare, that I'll wager you've never heard of it. It's — dragon stew!"

The king gasped. "That sounds different. What's in it — besides dragon, of course?"

"Oh, I can't tell you!" exclaimed Klaus. "It has been a secret in my family for thirteen generations."

"I understand," nodded the king, "but if we can ever locate a dragon, you must make it for me. However, you can begin preparing an ordinary royal banquet. You are the new royal cook."

Klaus bowed deeply. "And what would you like for dinner?" he asked.

"How about roast pig with applesauce?"

"And would your Majesty care to show me exactly how you want it cooked?" Klaus asked innocently.

The king stared. "You mean you won't care if I offer advice and suggestions? Why, you and I are going to get along just fine!"

So off they went to the kitchen and collected everything the king needed. Then Klaus said, "Now, how would you prepare this, your Majesty?"

King Chubby, greatly delighted, stuffed the pig, trussed it up, and then peeled and sliced the apples.

"How would you cook this, your Majesty?"

So the king happily popped the pig into the oven. He alternated between stirring the applesauce and basting and turning the pig.

Klaus watched and kept saying, "Just how I'd have done it. I use the same method."

When the pig was brown and savory and the sauce bubbling merrily, he said, "I thank you for all your suggestions, sire."

"If you will go to the banquet hall, I'll serve you the banquet I have prepared."

When the king had gobbled up the last piece of pork and soppet of sauce, he announced that it was the finest banquet he'd ever eaten and Klaus was the finest cook he'd ever had. And from then on, the king and his new cook were well satisfied — King Chubby because he now had all his favorite dishes cooked exactly as he liked them and Klaus because he was living off the best of the land.

One morning, a good many months after Klaus had become the royal cook, he was called to the throne room. When he entered, he was horrified to see the Captain of the guard and a dozen scratched and smoke-blackened soldiers surrounding a large cage inside of which was a small, fat dragon.

"Surprise!" beamed the king. "I sent them out to find a dragon months ago, and it's taken all this time to find one. Now you can cook your special dragon stew tonight. I promise I won't try to find out your secret — I won't even set foot in the kitchen today!"

The soldiers carried the cage to the kitchen, set it down, and trooped out. The Captain said, "Careful of him, Cook — he bites, scratches, and can shoot fire six inches out of his nose."

Klaus stared at the small dragon. A tear trickled down its cheek. "Are you trying to think of the best way to kill me?" it asked, accusingly. "It isn't fair! I was minding my own business, bothering no one, and suddenly your soldiers attacked me and carried me here to be made into — into stew." He sniffled.

321

"Believe me, dragon," said Klaus, "I don't want to make you into stew. I didn't think there were any dragons when I made up that silly recipe. I just wanted to fool the king into thinking I was a cook. I couldn't make any stew if my life depended on it — and it probably does. The king will have me beheaded when he finds out that I fooled him."

"Oh, making stew is easy," said the dragon. "You soak the meat in wine and spices, brown it in butter and simmer it slowly in broth with onions and carrots. I always throw in a few mushrooms and some parsley, too. And then . . ."

"You can cook?" interrupted Klaus. "I thought dragons only ate raw princesses and things like that."

"Heavens, no!" the dragon shuddered.

"Actually, I'm a good cook. Living alone, I've had to do all my own cooking. I've become quite a chef, if I do say so myself." He blew a smoke ring from his left nostril.

Suddenly, Klaus began to grin and nod his head as though he had thought of something.

At seven o'clock, the king hurried into the banquet hall, tingling to taste Klaus' wonderful dragon stew. He watched eagerly as Klaus carried in a steaming bowl and ladled chunks of beautifully browned meat and vegetables swimming in rich gravy onto the king's plate. King Chubby began to gobble. After four helpings, he leaned back with a sigh.

"That certainly is one of the best stews I've ever eaten. What a shame we can never have it again. That was probably the world's last dragon."

"Oh, we can have it as often as you like, your Majesty," Klaus calmly announced. "You see, the thing that makes dragon stew such a rare recipe is that it can only be cooked *by* a dragon! Allow me to present my assistant."

Klaus whistled, and in came the dragon, wearing a tall, white cook's hat and a gravystained apron. He bowed deeply.

"Under my direction," said Klaus with a charming grin, "my assistant will be happy to make dragon stew whenever you want it."

So everything turned out very well. King Chubby was able to cook his own banquets just as he liked them. He could also have dragon stew (made from beef) as often as he wanted it. Klaus was happy to be living off the best of the land without having to work hard for it. The dragon was delighted to be an assistant royal cook.

But the happiest of all was the kitchen helper. One of his jobs had been to light the fire in the big stove, and he had always scorched his knuckles. But now he no longer had this task, for the assistant cook lit his own stove by shooting fire out of his nose!

Author

Tom McGowen is a writer, an artist, and an editor. He has also had a variety of jobs in advertising. Mr. McGowen has written over twenty books for children. Some of them are humorous picture books like *Dragon Stew,* and others are books for older readers. His attractive science books, such as *Album of Dinosaurs* and *Album of Sharks*, are always well worn in libraries and are very popular. His book *Album of Whales* was chosen as an Outstanding Science Trade Book for Children in 1980.

Josephine's 'Magination

Written and illustrated by Arnold Dobrin

"If you're going to come with me to market you better get a move on," Josephine's mother called. Then she added — just in case Josephine might still dawdle on the way, "You hear me, girl? I'm going to market *now.*"

Josephine put down her flower dolls and brushed the dirt off her skirt. She rushed into the house to get a drink of water, tried to brush some more dirt off her dress and then ran down the path. Already her mother was turning the bend in the road past the palmettos. Her back was straight as a board because on her head she carried the big basket of brooms she took each Friday morning to market.

Oh, it was hot — it was terribly hot! And it would be that way for a long time. It would stay that way through most of the day. But then, when the shadows started to get big, a cool, soft breeze would gently drift in from the sea. And that would feel so good.

About that time — if all the brooms were sold — Josephine's mother would give her some pennies to spend on whatever she wanted. Candy? Sweet jellied-rolls? It was always hard for Josephine to decide. But awfully nice to think about on and off throughout the day.

"Bonjour Lucille," said a woman who suddenly came out of a path on her way to town. She carried a heavy load of fruit to sell and already she looked hot.

"Bonjour Francoise," called Josephine's mother.

"Going to be a very hot day," Francoise sighed.

"It's going to be that, all right," Josephine's mother said as they walked, single-file, down the dusty path. As they talked, Josephine fell behind. She let her feet move slowly in the warm, soft dust of the path and thought about those pennies she might get at the end of the day.

It was good to buy jelly rolls or candy but it would be a lot better to buy a doll — a real doll. Josephine never had a real doll. She'd had flower dolls — like those she played with that morning. But they were just hibiscus flower dolls.

Her mother had showed her how to make them when she was very small. She showed her how to take a tiny sliver of wood and stick it into a hibiscus bud. That was the head. The rest of the stick went into a big flower turned upside down. That made the skirt.

They were pretty, yes, and delicate too. But they wilted so soon. Josephine would make them fresh and bright in the morning, but by noon their heads would shrivel and their skirts would look torn and shaggy.

Josephine wished she could have a real doll someday.

After a while another woman turned into the dusty path with a load of baskets. "Bonjour Lucille," she called to Josephine's mother.

"Bonjour Gabrielle," came the answer.

"Going to be sizzling hot today!" Gabrielle said.

"Sure is," Josephine's mother agreed.

Josephine and her mother walked along the dusty path. Francoise and Gabrielle walked along not far behind. In a little while they met another woman with a big load of mangoes on her head.

"Bonjour Marie," said Josephine's mother.

"Fine morning to you," Marie said as she joined the group of women going to town. In a little while they met a man with a wheelbarrow full of grain. Soon they met other men too — men with burros or goats. One man tugged at a stubborn pig. Everybody had something to sell at the market. Nobody went with empty hands — except Josephine.

When you go to market you've got to have something to sell.

Josephine was getting tired. She wanted to lie down in the shade of some palm trees along the edge of the path. She wanted a sip of cool water. She was almost sorry she'd agreed to go to the market. If she hadn't she would now be at home playing with her flower dolls. But even if she stayed at home there would be chores to do. She could just hear her mother saying — as she so often did — "Now Josephine, work is one thing and play is another. We got to get these brooms to market and we got to sell every one of them!"

Josephine wriggled her toes in the dusty path and hoped they would be there soon.

Around the bend in the road Josephine could smell the market place. It was a strong good smell of sweet fruit and vegetables, candies and frying pork, of goats and pigs and straw and dust.

Josephine walked faster now. She followed her mother to their favorite spot in a little patch of shade under a torn awning. Carefully Josephine's mother lowered the basket of little brooms from her head and set it before her as she sat down. Now her little shop was in order. She didn't have one thing more to do except sit and sell brooms until the sun went down.

"Now you run off, child," Josephine's mother said as she gave her a playful little push. "I have business to attend to."

Josephine wandered through the big, noisy market. All along the sides of the square were little shops where people were busy buying or selling or cooking or making things.

Josephine loved the shop with a sign that said, "The Fine Sweet Shop." It smelled of fresh baked goods — bread and cakes and little sweet tarts. Josephine watched the baker working in the little room just beyond. How busily and expertly he worked with the brightly-colored frostings — shaping, pushing, forming the delicious things to eat. How quickly he worked. What good use he made of everything around him! Nothing was wasted — nothing at all.

Next door was the butcher shop. The butcher was working hard too. All of his knives were gleaming and sharp. They flashed in the bright sunlight as he carefully carved his meats.

That was the way it was with all of the people who came to market. Everybody worked hard — nothing was wasted, everything was used.

Josephine had just turned away from the butcher shop when she bumped into an old man she had never seen before. He had a big stick and a very big straw hat — much bigger than those anyone else wore. On it were different little animals made of straw. There were monkeys and pigs, donkeys and roosters. Some of them had tiny, jingly bells attached or were decorated with bright strips of cloth.

Josephine almost lost her balance but then she felt two big strong hands holding her up. "Looks like you have bumped into good luck, young lady!" The old man cackled and pulled one of the little straw pigs off his hat. "Here, child," he said, "I don't want to see those big, frightened eyes of yours first thing this market day. I want to start off with a *smile*. Come on now, child. Let me see a good big smile. That's the *only* way to start off market day!"

Josephine smiled and said, "Thank you," as she took the pretty thing in her hand. She was about to run to her mother when she had a thought. She turned to the old man saying, "How did you learn to make little animals of straw like that?"

The old man cackled again and grinned broadly. He slapped his knee, straightened up and had a good long laugh.

"Why, child," he said, good-naturedly, "Nobody taught me how to do it. Nobody learned me how to do much of anything. I just used my 'magination!"

Toward afternoon the shadows started to get big. The cool, soft breeze started to drift in from the sea. Josephine ran back to where her mother was sitting in the shade of the torn awning.

"Look, maman, *look* what a man gave me!"

Josephine's mother took the pig and examined it closely. "Cute little thing," she said, but then she

sighed wearily. Josephine saw that only about half of
the brooms were gone. "Guess we better start getting
home," her mother said as she felt around for her hat.
"This just isn't much of a broom day!" But then she
fished under her skirt for the little black bag where
she kept her money. She pulled out a penny — just
one penny. "I guess you need something sweet in
your mouth before we start for home. Now — run
off to that Fine Sweet Shop."

Josephine rushed to the candy and cake store. On
her way she passed the stall where the dolls were sold.
But she tried not to look at them, tried not to think
about them. For one penny she could only get one
piece of candy so she chose carefully. Finally she
decided on a nice piece of hard, lime candy — tangy

but sweet — and cool like the breeze that was softly blowing in from the sea.

The sun was setting. The wind from the sea grew stronger. Josephine thought that this was one of the best times of market day — just going home. In the east, the moon hung in the sky like a big, pale slice of melon. The palmettos whispered and scratched against each other in the evening sea breeze. And the dust of the road felt cool and soft and easy to walk on.

As soon as Josephine got home she ran to see her flower dolls. They were so wilted and ugly that she was sorry she had kept them. She swept them angrily off the table onto the floor and went to help her mother prepare dinner.

They ate baked yams, breadfruit, mangoes and had sugar cane for dessert. Josephine was so hungry that every bite tasted delicious. "Never saw a child eat so much in my life!" her mother said.

But after she had eaten, the only thing that she could think about was her bed. Lying down in a darkened corner of the room, she thought about the day just passed.

She thought about the long, dusty walk into town and the walk back under the moon that seemed even longer. She thought about all the people and the shops and the happy old man with the straw toys attached to his big hat. How clearly she could hear him saying in a laughing voice, "I just used my 'magination!"

Josephine reached out to feel in the pocket of her dress for the straw pig. In the firelight she could only see its outlines but she could feel the smoothly-woven straw and try to imagine what it looked like.

Did Josephine have a "'magination?" Maybe she did and maybe she didn't. She wondered how you got a 'magination if you didn't already have one. Josephine decided she had to find out if she had one. Just before she went to sleep she promised herself that she wouldn't let another day pass without finding out if she too had a 'magination.

The morning was still cool when Josephine awoke. She looked at the bright, long stripes of morning sunlight falling on the floor of their tiny one-room house. In the far corner of the room her mother was sleeping soundly on her bed of straw matting. Outside, the birds were busy calling to each other and getting their breakfasts. Far down near the shore she heard a man's voice shouting. He was probably a fisherman busy getting his boat ready to take out to sea.

Busy, busy, busy — people were getting busy. That made her remember. She too should be getting busy. She had to find out about her 'magination.

Josephine looked around the room again and again. She tried to make some 'magination thoughts come into her head. She tried very hard to think. To see if she could find something — or *two* different things — that she could make something *new* out of.

There in a corner were short, broken broom
handles. Nearby were the scratchy straw parts of the
brooms. And scissors and raffia. Josephine looked at
them for a long time.

Almost before she knew what she was doing,
Josephine jumped out of bed and tied one of the
straw brooms to a broken broom. Then she took
some scissors and cut the straws short.

How funny it looked now — not like a broom at
all but like a skirt.

"What are you doing there?" Her mother raised
herself from her straw mat.

"Just playing."

"Just playing? Well, why are you playing with my
good brooms? You answer me that!"

"But Maman, this one was broken. You never use the broken ones."

"But I use the rest of what you're using. Now you get dressed and get us some eggs. We got to have our breakfast!"

Josephine slid the little broom under her bed of mats and did as her mother told her. After that there was other work to do. She had to weed the vegetable garden and feed the chickens. During the heat of the day she slept for a long time. When she awoke in the late afternoon she thought maybe she would make some fresh flower dolls. But she didn't. She was tired of those old floppy, withery dolls. Toward evening it was time to go down to the shore to buy a piece of fish for their supper.

It was a day just like a lot of other days. But Josephine felt a new kind of happy feeling all through the day. She didn't understand why or how — but she felt it.

That night when Josephine went to bed she put the strange little broom next to her on the pillow. In the moonlight it looked very strange. It wasn't a doll — but it was *almost* a doll.

Josephine listened to the rising of the night sea wind. Sometimes it rattled their shaky little house so much that she thought it would fall down on her. She reached out and felt the strange little doll. She was glad it was there.

The sky was just starting to get light when Josephine heard the first rooster crowing.

"Cocka-doodle-doo. Cocka-doodle-doo . . ." He was better than any clock because he woke her at just about the same time every morning. It was going to be a beautiful morning. But Josephine didn't have time to watch the long, bright fingers of sunlight crawl into the room today.

Without even thinking what she was doing, she ran to the shed where her mother kept some paint. She took an old brush and quickly covered the broom handle with black paint. She worked quickly without thinking very much how. She knew what she had to do. Something was telling her. She knew it was her 'magination giving out the orders.

As soon as the paint had dried, Josephine took some brightly-colored scraps of cloth that were left over from a dress Josephine's mother had made for her. One of the strips got tied around the middle of the broom-doll. The other was bound around her head in the same way that some of the women on the island bound their heads.

Josephine put the broom-doll down and looked at it. It was amazing what 'magination could tell you to do — no doubt about it! But something important was still missing. Josephine picked a long, feathery weed which made a fine-pointed brush. A good dab of red made the mouth. White showed where the eyes were.

Oh yes, now she was wonderful. She was a doll, a *real* doll. But she was more than a doll too. Just take her in your fingers and brush her back and forth and she worked hard cleaning and sweeping for you! What a good, busy kind of doll — not just one that lay around the house all day waiting to be taken care of.

"Show me what you got there!" her mother's voice suddenly commanded from her dark corner of the room.

"I made a doll, Maman," Josephine said, taking the broom-doll to show her mother.

"Well . . . I never seen such a thing before." Her mother smiled. "Why, Josephine, you made yourself a mighty cute little doll."

"And Maman," Josephine said, "she's a good worker too!" She showed her mother what a good sweeping her doll could do.

"Yes — and a good worker too!" her mother agreed. "Josephine — you're a mighty smart little girl."

That afternoon they decided to make more broom-dolls so they could take them to market on

Friday morning. Josephine's mother made the brooms as usual but Josephine painted their faces. And part of her job was also to tie on the brightly-colored pieces around their middles and on their heads.

When Friday morning came, Josephine and her mother were out of bed early and on their way into town while the morning was still cool. Hardly anyone was at the market place when they arrived. And it seemed that hours and hours went by — a long, long time — until anyone even came to see the strange little broom-dolls.

But then people began to come to look at them. And after they touched and admired the dolls they began to buy them. The children came too and begged their parents to buy some dolls. To them it didn't matter that the dolls were such good workers. They just liked the way they looked.

Josephine watched with delight as the little black purse began to fill with coins. She knew there would be candy this afternoon — perhaps more than ever before. She was just thinking about what she would choose when she saw a big shadow on the ground before her.

It was the shadow of the big straw hat that the old toy man wore. First he looked at the brooms, then at Josephine.

He said, "I seen you before. You're the little girl who bumped into me the other day."

"Yes, I'm the girl," Josephine said.

The toy man's smile broadened. "And you made these dolls? I never seen such dolls before!"

"My mother and I made them," Josephine said.

He took one, turned it around admiringly. "Child — I'd say you got a powerful 'magination."

Josephine smiled.

Author

Arnold Dobrin says that when he was in third grade in Los Angeles, he began to think of himself as an artist. Later he became a writer, too.

Among his many books are *Taro and the Sea Turtles*, *Gilly Gilhooley: a Tale of Ireland*, *Scat!*, and *Jillions of Gerbils*.

The Tales of
Olga da Polga

Michael Bond
Author of A BEAR CALLED PADDINGTON

Illustrated by Hans Helweg

Houghton Mifflin Literature

In each story you just read, someone had a good idea. Olga Da Polga has lots of them!

Olga is a guinea pig who uses her clever ideas and quick thinking to make the best of any situation. You will enjoy the entertaining stories she tells in *The Tales of Olga Da Polga* by Michael Bond.

8

Changes

ANNIE
AND THE
OLD ONE

BY MISKA MILES

ILLUSTRATED BY
WINFIELD COLEMAN

Annie's Navajo world was good — a world of rippling sand, of high copper-red bluffs in the distance, of the low mesa near her own snug hogan. The pumpkins were yellow in the cornfield, and the tassels on the corn were turning brown.

Each morning, the gate to the night pen near the hogan was opened wide and the sheep were herded to pasture on the desert.

Annie helped watch the sheep. She carried pails of water to the cornfield. And every weekday, she walked to the bus stop and waited for the yellow bus that took her to school and brought her home again.

Best of all were the evenings when she sat at her grandmother's feet and listened to stories of times long gone.

Sometimes it seemed to Annie that her grandmother was her age — a girl who had seen no more than nine or ten harvestings.

If a mouse skittered and jerked across the hard dirt floor of their hogan, Annie and her grandmother laughed together.

And when they prepared the fried bread for the evening meal, if it burned a bit black at the edges, they laughed and said it was good.

There were other times when her grandmother sat small and still, and Annie knew that she was very old. Then Annie would cover the thin knees of the Old One with a warm blanket.

It was at such a time that her grandmother said, "It is time you learn to weave, my granddaughter."

Annie touched the web of wrinkles that criss-crossed her grandmother's face and slowly went outside the hogan.

Beside the door, her father sat cross-legged, working with silver and fire, making a handsome, heavy necklace. Annie passed him and went to the big loom where her mother sat weaving.

Annie sat beside the loom, watching, while her mother slid the weaving stick in place among the strings of the warp. With red wool, her mother added a row to a slanting arrow of red, bright against the dull background.

Annie's thoughts wandered. She thought about the stories her grandmother had told — stories of hardship when rains flooded the desert — of dry weather when rains did not fall and the pumpkins and corn were dry in the field.

Annie looked out across the sand where the cactus bore its red fruit, and thought about the coyote — God's Dog — guarding the scattered hogans of the Navajos.

Annie watched while her mother worked. She made herself sit very still.

After a time, her mother looked at her and smiled. "Are you ready to weave, my daughter?"

Annie shook her head.

She continued to watch while her mother twisted the weaving stick in the warp, making a shed for the strands of gray and red wool.

At last her mother said softly, "You may go," almost as though she knew what Annie wanted.

Annie ran off to find her grandmother, and together they gathered twigs and brush to feed the small fire in the middle of the hogan.

When the evening meal was done, the old grandmother called her family together.

Annie and her mother and father stood quietly, respectfully, waiting for the grandmother to speak.

A coyote called shrilly from the mesa.

There was no sound in the hogan. There was no sound at all, except a small snap of the dying fire.

Then the grandmother spoke softly.

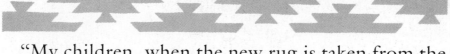

"My children, when the new rug is taken from the loom, I will go to Mother Earth."

Annie shivered and looked at her mother.

Her mother's eyes were shining bright with tears that did not fall, and Annie knew what her grandmother meant. Her heart stood still and she made no sound.

The Old One spoke again.

"You will each choose the gift that you wish to have."

Annie looked at the hard earth, swept smooth and clean.

"What will you have, my granddaughter?" the grandmother asked.

Annie looked at a weaving stick propped against the wall of the hogan. This was the grandmother's own weaving stick, polished and beautiful with age. Annie looked directly at the stick.

As though Annie had spoken, her grandmother nodded.

"My granddaughter shall have my weaving stick."

On the floor of the hogan lay a rug that the Old One had woven long, long ago. Its colors were mellowed and its warp and weft were strong.

Annie's mother chose the rug.

Annie's father chose the silver belt studded with turquoise that was now loose around the small waist of the Old One.

Annie folded her arms tightly across her stomach and went outside, and her mother followed.

"How can my grandmother know she will go to Mother Earth when the rug is taken from the loom?" Annie asked.

"Many of the Old Ones know," her mother said.

"How do they know?"

"Your grandmother is one of those who live in harmony with all nature — with earth, coyote, birds in the sky. They know more than many will ever learn. Those Old Ones know." Her mother sighed deeply. "We will speak of other things."

In the days that followed, the grandmother went about her work much as she had always done.

She ground corn to make meal for bread.

She gathered dry twigs and brush to make fire.

And when there was no school, she and Annie watched the sheep and listened to the sweet, clear music of the bell on the collar of the lead goat.

The weaving of the rug was high on the loom. It was almost as high as Annie's waist.

"My mother," Annie said, "why do you weave?"

"I weave so we may sell the rug and buy the things we must have from the trading post. Silver for silvermaking. Deer hide for boots — "

"But you know what my grandmother said — "

Annie's mother did not speak. She slid her weaving stick through the warp and picked up a strand of rose-red wool.

Annie turned and ran. She ran across the sand and huddled in the shallow shade of the small mesa.

Her grandmother would go back to the earth when the rug was taken from the loom. The rug must not be finished. Her mother must not weave.

The next morning, where her grandmother went, Annie followed.

When it was time to go to the bus stop to meet the school bus, she dawdled, walking slowly and watching her feet. Perhaps she would miss the bus.

And then quite suddenly she did not want to miss it. She knew what she must do.

She ran hard, as fast as she could — breathing deeply — and the yellow bus was waiting for her at the stop.

She climbed aboard. The bus moved on, stopping now and then at hogans along the way. Annie sat there alone and made her plan.

In school, she would be bad, so bad that the teacher would send for her mother and father.

And if her mother and father came to school to talk to the teacher, that would be one day when her mother could not weave. One day.

On the playground, Annie's teacher was in charge of the girls' gymnasium class.

"Who will lead the exercises today?" the teacher asked.

No one answered.

The teacher laughed. "Very well. Then I shall be leader." The teacher was young, with yellow hair. Her blue skirt was wide and the heels on her brown shoes were high. The teacher kicked off her shoes and the girls laughed.

Annie followed the teacher's lead — bending, jumping, and she waited for the time when the teacher would lead them in jogging around the playground.

As Annie jogged past the spot where the teacher's shoes lay on the ground, she picked up a shoe and hid it in the folds of her dress.

And when Annie jogged past a trash can, she dropped the shoe inside.

Some of the girls saw her and laughed, but some frowned and were solemn.

When the line jogged near the schoolhouse door, Annie slipped from the line and went inside to her room and her own desk.

Clearly she heard the teacher as she spoke to the girls outside.

"The other shoe, please." Her voice was pleasant. There was silence.

Limping, one shoe on and one shoe gone, the teacher came into the room.

The girls followed, giggling and holding their hands across their mouths.

"I know it's funny," the teacher said, "but now I need the shoe."

Annie looked at the boards of the floor. A shiny black beetle crawled between the cracks.

The door opened and a man teacher came inside with a shoe in his hand. As he passed Annie's desk, he touched her shoulder and smiled down at her.

"I saw someone playing tricks," he said.

The teacher looked at Annie and the room was very still.

When school was over for the day, Annie waited.

Timidly, with hammering heart, she went to the teacher's desk.

"Do you want my mother and father to come to the school tomorrow?" she asked.

"No, Annie," the teacher said. "I have the shoe. Everything is all right."

Annie's face was hot and her hands were cold. She turned and ran. She was the last to climb on the bus.

Finally, there was her own bus stop. She hopped down and slowly trudged the long way home. She stopped beside the loom.

The rug was now much higher than her waist.

That night she curled up in her blanket. She slept lightly, and awakened before dawn.

There was no sound from her mother's sheepskin. Her grandmother was a quiet hump in her blanket. Annie heard only her father's loud, sleeping breathing. There was no other sound on the whole earth, except the howling of a coyote from far across the desert.

In the dim light of early morning, Annie crept outside to the night pen where the sheep were sleeping.

The dry wood creaked when she opened the gate and pushed it wide open against the fence.

She tugged at the sleeping sheep until one stood quietly. Then the others stood also, uncertain — shoving together. The lead goat turned toward the open gate and Annie slipped her fingers through his belled collar. She curled her fingertips across the bell, muffling its sound, and led the goat through the gate. The sheep followed.

She led them across the sand and around the small mesa where she released the goat.

"Go," she said.

She ran back to the hogan, and slithered under her blanket and lay shivering. Now her family would hunt the sheep all day. This would be a day when her mother would not weave.

When the fullness of morning came and it was light, Annie watched her grandmother rise and go outside.

Annie heard her call.

"The sheep are gone."

Annie's mother and father hurried outside and Annie followed.

Her mother moaned softly, "The sheep — the sheep — "

"I see them," the grandmother said. "They graze near the mesa."

Annie went with her grandmother and when they reached the sheep, Annie's fingers slipped under the goat's collar and the bell tingled sharply as the sheep followed back to the pen.

In school that day, Annie sat quietly and wondered what more she could do. When the teacher asked questions, Annie looked at the floor. She did not even hear.

When night came, she curled up in her blanket, but not to sleep.

When everything was still, she slipped from her blanket and crept outside.

The sky was dark and secret. The wind was soft against her face. For a moment she stood waiting until she could see in the night.

She went to the loom.

She felt for the weaving stick there in its place among the warp strings. She separated the warp and felt for the wool.

Slowly she pulled out the strands of yarn, one by one.

One by one, she laid them across her knees.

And when the row was removed, she separated the strings of the warp again, and reached for the second row.

When the woven rug was only as high as her waist, she crept back to her blanket, taking the strands of wool with her.

Under her blanket, she smoothed the strands and made them into a ball. And then she slept.

The next night, Annie removed another day's weaving.

In the morning when her mother went to the loom, she looked at the weaving — puzzled —

For a moment, she pressed her fingers against her eyes.

The Old One looked at Annie curiously. Annie held her breath.

The third night, Annie crept to the loom.

A gentle hand touched her shoulder.

"Go to sleep, my granddaughter," the Old One said.

Annie wanted to throw her arms around her grandmother's waist and tell her why she had been bad, but she could only stumble to her blanket and huddle under it and let the tears roll into the edge of her hair.

When morning came, Annie unrolled herself from the blanket and helped prepare the morning meal.

Afterward, she followed her grandmother through the cornfield. Her grandmother walked slowly, and Annie fitted her steps to the slow steps of the Old One.

When they reached the small mesa, the Old One sat crossing her knees, folding her gnarled fingers into her lap.

Annie knelt beside her.

The Old One looked far off toward the rim of desert where sky met sand.

"My granddaughter," she said, "you have tried to hold back time. This cannot be done." The desert stretched yellow and brown away to the edge of the morning sky. "The sun comes up from the edge of earth in the morning. It returns to the edge of earth in the evening. Earth, from which good things come for the living creatures on it. Earth, to which all creatures finally go."

Annie picked up a handful of brown sand and pressed it against the palm of her hand. Slowly, she let it fall to earth. She understood many things.

The sun rose but it also set.

The cactus did not bloom forever. Petals dried and fell to earth.

She knew that she was a part of the earth and the things on it. She would always be a part of the earth, just as her grandmother had always been, just as her grandmother would always be, always and forever.

And Annie was breathless with the wonder of it.

They walked back to the hogan together, Annie and the Old One.

Annie picked up the old weaving stick.

"I am ready to weave," she said to her mother. "I will use the stick that my grandmother has given me." She knelt at the loom.

She separated the warp strings and slipped the weaving stick in place, as her mother had done, as her grandmother had done.

She picked up a strand of gray wool and started to weave.

Author

This author has written many fine children's books under her pen name, Miska Miles, and under her real name, Patricia Miles Martin. She has been a teacher as well as an author of stories and poems. *Annie and the Old One,* winner of several book awards, was a Newbery Medal Honor Book.

My Grandmother Tells Me

by Ann Nolan Clark

My grandmother tells me,
  "For two summer moons
  I will walk with you
  across the sand patches,
  by the rock ridges
  and the cacti,
  through the dry washes
  and along the sandy trails
  that you may know the desert
  and hold its beauty
  in your heart forever."

THE EMPEROR'S PLUM TREE

Written and illustrated
by Michelle Nikly

Translated by Elizabeth Shub

Long ago, in the land of the rising sun, there lived an emperor whose garden was beautiful beyond imagination. Each tree, each flower, each stone had its place in the total harmony of the design.

One morning as the emperor took his daily stroll, he stopped in dismay at a grove of plum trees. Could that tree near the wall be dying? He hurried to it. He felt a twig. It broke off in his hand, brittle and dry. The tree would have to be cut down. The perfect garden would be perfect no longer. The emperor shut himself up in his palace and refused to go out.

Days passed, and indoors, the emperor mourned his garden. At last it was decided that only a plum tree as beautiful as the one that died could restore the garden and make the emperor happy again. Messengers were sent to search the land and within a day a perfect tree was found in the garden of a painter named Ukiyo.

Ukiyo, his wife Tanka, and their small son Musuko were desolate when they learned that their tree had been chosen for the imperial garden. Ukiyo loved to paint its gnarled branches and starlike flowers, and many of the poems Tanka wrote described its beauty.

But most of all, the plum tree was the home of Musuko's friend, the nightingale. Musuko often stood at the foot of the tree and spoke to her. She replied in her own way, yet they always understood one another as true friends do.

Ukiyo knew they had to part with the tree, but he asked if they might keep it one day longer.

When the plum tree was about to be taken away, Musuko approached the emperor's messenger. He asked if he might tie a scroll to one of its branches. The messenger, seeing how bravely the boy choked back his tears, lifted him up so that he could attach the scroll.

The plum tree was replanted in the imperial garden and the emperor was persuaded to come and see it. He gazed at it while the courtiers waited anxiously. At last, to everyone's relief, he smiled. The emperor's garden was flawless once again.
Then the emperor noticed Musuko's scroll. He took it down and unrolled it.

What he saw was a wonderfully lifelike drawing of a branch of the plum tree, and perched on the branch was a nightingale. Beneath the painting was a poem.

At the long day's end,
when the nightingale flies home,
what shall I tell her?

For a long time, the emperor stood in thought before the plum tree. Then he sent a messenger to bring Ukiyo, Tanka, and Musuko to the palace. The following day, they appeared before him. He spoke first to Musuko.

"My child," the emperor said, "I will tell you what to say to your homeless friend. Tell her that her plum tree, borrowed for a day because of the emperor's whim, will be returned to her by the emperor's order."

Ukiyo and Tanka were about to protest, but the emperor would not let them.

"It seems that my sorrow has been replaced by yours. I could not bear to see this tree each day, knowing that a child lost his friend because of me. This tree belongs in your garden, but before it leaves mine, I have a request. Ukiyo, I ask you to paint my garden, perfect as it is on this day."

"The death of my plum tree has reminded me that no garden can last forever. One day the peach trees, the pines, and even the bamboos will be no more. But your painting, Ukiyo, will be a lasting reminder of this garden's perfection."

"And, Tanka, I ask you to write this story, just as it happened, so that in times to come children will hear how once the Emperor of Japan learned wisdom from a small boy named Musuko, a nightingale, and a plum tree."

Author

Michelle Nikly, who lives in Europe, first wrote *The Emperor's Plum Tree* in French. After the book was published in France, a well known translator in New York, Elizabeth Shub, retold the story in English so that American children could enjoy it. Another of Ms. Nikly's books that you might enjoy is *The Princess on the Nut*.

PLUM TREES

by Rankō

So sweet the plum trees smell!
Would that the brush that paints the flower
Could paint the scent as well.

I come to look, and lo,
The plum tree petals scatter down
A fall of purest snow.

An excerpt from

Winnie-the-Pooh

by A. A. Milne

ILLUSTRATED BY
Ernest H. Shepard

In Which

Pooh Goes Visiting and Gets Into a Tight Place

Edward Bear, known to his friends as Winnie-the-Pooh, or Pooh for short, was walking through the forest one day, humming proudly to himself. He had made up a little hum that very morning, as he was doing his Stoutness Exercises in front of the glass: *Tra-la-la, tra-la-la,* as he stretched up as high as he could go, and then *Tra-la-la, tra-la — oh, help! — la,* as he tried to reach his toes. After breakfast he had said it over and over to himself until he had learnt it off by heart, and now he was humming it right through, properly. It went like this:

> *Tra-la-la, tra-la-la,*
> *Tra-la-la, tra-la-la,*
> *Rum-tum-tiddle-um-tum.*
> *Tiddle-iddle, tiddle-iddle,*
> *Tiddle-iddle, tiddle-iddle,*
> *Rum-tum-tum-tiddle-um.*

Well, he was humming this hum to himself, and walking along gaily, wondering what everybody else was doing, and what it felt like, being somebody else, when suddenly he came to a sandy bank, and in the bank was a large hole.

"Aha!" said Pooh. (*Rum-tum-tiddle-um-tum.*) "If I know anything about anything, that hole means Rabbit," he said, "and Rabbit means Company," he said, "and Company means Food and Listening-to Me-Humming and such like. *Rum-tum-tum-tiddle-um.*"

So he bent down, put his head into the hole, and called out:

"Is anybody at home?"

There was a sudden scuffling noise from inside the hole, and then silence.

"What I said was, 'Is anybody at home?'" called out Pooh very loudly.

"No!" said a voice; and then added, "You needn't shout so loud. I heard you quite well the first time."

"Bother!" said Pooh. "Isn't there anybody here at all?"

"Nobody."

Winnie-the-Pooh took his head out of the hole, and thought for a little, and he thought to himself, "There must be somebody there, because somebody must have *said* 'Nobody.'" So he put his head back in the hole, and said:

"Hallo, Rabbit, isn't that you?"

"No," said Rabbit, in a different sort of voice this time.

"But isn't that Rabbit's voice?"

"I don't *think* so," said Rabbit. "It isn't *meant* to be."

"Oh!" said Pooh.

He took his head out of the hole, and had another think, and then he put it back, and said:

"Well, could you very kindly tell me where Rabbit is?"

"He has gone to see his friend Pooh Bear, who is a great friend of his."

"But this *is* Me!" said Bear, very much surprised.

"What sort of Me?"

"Pooh Bear."

"Are you sure?" said Rabbit, still more surprised.

"Quite, quite sure," said Pooh.

"Oh, well, then, come in."

So Pooh pushed and pushed and pushed his way through the hole, and at last he got in.

"You were quite right," said Rabbit, looking at him all over. "It *is* you. Glad to see you."

"Who did you think it was?"

"Well, I wasn't sure. You know how it is in the Forest. One can't have *anybody* coming into one's house. One has to be *careful*. What about a mouthful of something?"

Pooh always liked a little something at eleven o'clock in the morning, and he was very glad to see Rabbit getting out the plates and mugs; and when Rabbit said, "Honey or condensed milk with your bread?" he was so excited that he said, "Both," and then, so as not to seem greedy, he added, "But don't bother about the bread, please." And for a long time after that he said nothing . . . until at last, humming to himself in a rather sticky voice, he got up, shook Rabbit lovingly by the paw, and said that he must be going on.

"Must you?" said Rabbit politely.

"Well," said Pooh, "I could stay a little longer if it — if you ——" and he tried very hard to look in the direction of the larder.

"As a matter of fact," said Rabbit, "I was going out myself directly."

"Oh, well, then, I'll be going on. Good-bye."

"Well, good-bye, if you're sure you won't have any more."

"*Is* there any more?" asked Pooh quickly.

Rabbit took the covers off the dishes, and said, "No, there wasn't."

"I thought not," said Pooh, nodding to himself. "Well, good-bye. I must be going on."

So he started to climb out of the hole. He pulled with his front paws, and pushed with his back paws, and in a little while his nose was out in the open again . . . and then his ears . . . and then his front paws . . . and then his shoulders . . . and then ——

"Oh, help!" said Pooh. "I'd better go back."

"Oh, bother!" said Pooh. "I shall have to go on."

"I can't do either!" said Pooh. "Oh, help *and* bother!"

Now by this time Rabbit wanted to go for a walk too, and finding the front door full, he went out by the back door, and came round to Pooh, and looked at him.

"Hallo, are you stuck?" he asked.

"N-no," said Pooh carelessly. "Just resting and thinking and humming to myself."

"Here, give us a paw."

Pooh Bear stretched out a paw, and Rabbit pulled and pulled and pulled. . . .

"*Ow!*" cried Pooh. "You're hurting!"

"The fact is," said Rabbit, "you're stuck."

"It all comes," said Pooh crossly, "of not having front doors big enough."

"It all comes," said Rabbit sternly, "of eating too much. I thought at the time," said Rabbit, "only I didn't like to say anything," said Rabbit, "that one of us was eating too much," said Rabbit, "and I knew it wasn't *me*," he said. "Well, well, I shall go and fetch Christopher Robin."

Christopher Robin lived at the other end of the Forest, and when he came back with Rabbit, and saw the front half of Pooh, he said, "Silly old Bear," in such a loving voice that everybody felt quite hopeful again.

"I was just beginning to think," said Bear, sniffing slightly, "that Rabbit might never be able to use his front door again. And I should *hate* that," he said.

"So should I," said Rabbit.

"Use his front door again?" said Christopher Robin. "Of course he'll use his front door again."

"Good," said Rabbit.

"If we can't pull you out, Pooh, we might push you back."

Rabbit scratched his whiskers thoughtfully, and pointed out that, when once Pooh was pushed back, he was back, and of course nobody was more glad to see Pooh than *he* was, still there it was, some lived in trees and some lived underground, and ——

"You mean I'd *never* get out?" said Pooh.

"I mean," said Rabbit, "that having got *so* far, it seems a pity to waste it."

Christopher Robin nodded.

"Then there's only one thing to be done," he said. "We shall have to wait for you to get thin again."

"How long does getting thin take?" asked Pooh anxiously.

"About a week, I should think."

"But I can't stay here for a *week!*"

"You can *stay* here all right, silly old Bear. It's getting you out which is so difficult."

"We'll read to you," said Rabbit cheerfully. "And I hope it won't snow," he added. "And I say, old fellow, you're taking up a good deal of room in my house — *do* you mind if I use your back legs as a towel-horse? Because, I mean, there they are — doing nothing — and it would be very convenient just to hang the towels on them."

"A week!" said Pooh gloomily. *"What about meals?"*

"I'm afraid no meals," said Christopher Robin, "because of getting thin quicker. But we *will* read to you."

Bear began to sigh, and then found he couldn't because he was so tightly stuck; and a tear rolled down his eye, as he said:

"Then would you read a Sustaining Book, such as would help and comfort a Wedged Bear in Great Tightness?"

So for a week Christopher Robin read that sort of book at the North end of Pooh, and Rabbit hung his washing on the South end . . . and in between Bear felt himself getting slenderer and slenderer. And at the end of the week Christopher Robin said, *"Now!"*

So he took hold of Pooh's front paws and Rabbit took hold of Christopher Robin, and all Rabbit's friends and relations took hold of Rabbit, and they all pulled together. . . .

And for a long time Pooh only said *"Ow!"* . . .

And *"Oh!"* . . .

And then, all of a sudden, he said *"Pop!"* just as if a cork were coming out of a bottle.

And Christopher Robin and Rabbit and all Rabbit's friends and relations went head-over-heels backwards . . . and on the top of them came Winnie-the-Pooh — free!

So, with a nod of thanks to his friends, he went on with his walk through the forest, humming proudly to himself. But, Christopher Robin looked after him lovingly, and said to himself, "Silly old Bear!"

Author

A. A. Milne was born in London in 1882. He wrote four books about Christopher Robin and his friends. *Winnie-the-Pooh* and *The House at Pooh Corner* are collections of stories. *When We Were Very Young* and *Now We Are Six* are books of poems. Mr. Milne wrote many plays, poems, and stories for adults, but he is remembered most for his Christopher Robin books.

Phoebe's Revolt

NATALIE BABBITT

➥ *Houghton Mifflin Literature* ➥

Changes are sometimes difficult as you found out in the stories you just read.

Phoebe's Revolt by Natalie Babbitt is a story about a young girl in England. Phoebe's amusing attempts to change the customs of the early 1900's are not met with approval.

Glossary

This glossary can help you learn the meanings and pronunciations of many words in this book. The meanings of the words as they are used in this book are always given. Often you will also find other common meanings listed.

You can find out the correct pronunciation of any glossary word by using the special spelling and the pronunciation key. The *Full Pronunciation Key* below shows how to pronounce each consonant and vowel in a special spelling. A short form of this key is at the bottom of every left-hand page.

Full Pronunciation Key

Consonant Sounds

b	**bib**	k	**c**at, **kick**	sh	di**sh**, **sh**ip
ch	**church**	l	**l**id, need**l**e	t	**t**igh**t**
d	**deed**	m	a**m**, **m**an	th	pa**th**, **th**in
f	**f**ast, o**ff**	n	**n**o, sudde**n**	*th*	**the**
g	**g**a**g**	ng	thi**ng**	v	ca**v**e, **v**ine
h	**h**at	p	**p**o**p**	w	**w**ith
hw	**wh**ich	r	**r**oa**r**	y	**y**es
j	**judge**	s	mi**ss**, **s**ee	z	**s**ize, **z**ebra
				zh	vi**s**ion

Vowel Sounds

ă	p**a**t	î	d**ear**, f**ier**ce	ŭ	c**u**t
ā	p**ay**	ŏ	p**o**t	û	f**ur**
â	**air**, c**are**	ō	g**o**	yoo	**u**se
ä	f**a**ther	ô	p**aw,** f**or**	ə	**a**go, it**e**m,
ĕ	p**e**t	oi	b**oy**, n**oi**se, **oi**l		penc**i**l, at**o**m
ē	b**e**	ŏŏ	b**oo**k		circ**u**s
ĭ	p**i**t	oo	b**oo**t	ər	butt**er**
ī	b**y**, p**ie**	ou	c**ow**, **ou**t		

Pronunciation key © 1986 by Houghton Mifflin Company. Adapted and reprinted by permission from the *Houghton Mifflin Primary Dictionary* and the *Houghton Mifflin Intermediate Dictionary.*

A

ac·count (ə **kount′**) Written records of money spent or received.

ac·cuse (ə **kyōōz′**) Blame for wrongdoing: *When he heard the window break, the man looked accusingly at the children playing baseball nearby.*

af·fect (ə **fĕkt′**) To bring about a change in: *The weather affects my moods.*

aisle (īl) A narrow path for walking between rows of seats or shelves.

al·ter·nate (ôl′ tər nāt′) To make something happen by turns, first one thing, then another: *The painter alternated green paint and red paint.*

an·noyed (ə **noid′**) Bothered; irritated: *He was annoyed by the dog's barking.*

ant·ler (ănt′ lər) A bony growth on the head of a deer or other animal. Antlers usually grow in pairs and are often branched.

anx·ious (ăngk′ shəs) Feeling nervous or uncertain about something: *We listened anxiously to the weather report the day the hurricane was predicted.*

ap·pe·tite (ăp′ ĭ tīt′) The desire for food: *After the long climb we had a big appetite.*

ap·pre·ci·ate (ə **prē′** shē āt′) To understand the worth or importance of something; to value highly.

a·re·na (ə **rē′** nə) A covered or open area for sports events or large shows.

a·ro·ma (ə **rō′** mə) Smell; fragrance: *We sniffed the aroma of hot apple pie.*

as·sis·tant (ə **sĭs′** tənt) Someone who helps.

as·so·ci·ate (ə **sō′** shē ĭt′) One member of a group that works together.

as·ton·ished (ə **stŏn′** ĭsht) Greatly surprised: *So many people had entered the contest, I was astonished when I won the prize.*

at·tack (ə **tăk′**) To make a sudden move against.

at·ten·tion (ə **tĕn′** shən) The act of noticing or giving care: *We paid careful attention to the speaker.*

awk·ward (ôk′ wərd) Clumsy: *I moved awkwardly in the duck costume.*

awn·ing (ô′ nĭng) A piece of material put up over a door or window to provide shade.

B

bade (băd) *or* (bād) Commanded; directed; asked: *The woman bade me to close the door.*

baf·fled (băf′ əld) Confused; puzzled: *Even my mother was baffled by my math homework.*

ban·is·ter (băn′ ĭ stər) The railing along a staircase.

ban·quet (băng′ kwĭt) A large meal, usually to celebrate something special.

bar·na·cle (bär′ nə kəl) A small, hard-shelled sea animal that attaches itself to rocks and to the bottoms of ships.

bar·on (băr′ ən) In the Middle Ages, a person who received lands and a title from the king.

bass (băs) A North American fish used for food.

bay (bā) A part of the sea that is partly surrounded by land.

beach·comb·er (bēch′ kō′ mər) Someone who walks the seashore looking for things that can be used: *The beachcomber found a piece of wood that looked like a shark.*

be·drag·gled (bĭ drăg′ əld) Limp and messy; looking as if it had been dragged through the mud: *The puppy looked bedraggled after it had been out in the rain.*

be·hav·ior (bĭ hăv′ yər) The way in which a person acts: *Talking when someone else is talking is rude behavior.*

bel·low (běl′ ō) To make a loud roar.

be·wil·dered (bĭ wĭl′ dərd) Confused; puzzled.

bold (bōld) Seeming to have no fear; brave: *The small child walked boldly onto the stage.*

boul·der (bōl′ dər) A large rounded rock.

bound (bound) **1.** Past tense of the word *bind*. Tied securely; Fastened. **2.** To leap; to jump: *The dog bounded into the air and caught the ball.* **3.** Heading for; going to: *The bus is bound for New York.*

Braille (brāl) A system of writing for blind people. A person reads Braille by feeling patterns of dots with the fingertips.

ă pat / ā pay / â care / ä father / ĕ pet / ē be / ĭ pit / ī pie / î fierce / ŏ pot / ō go
ô paw, for / oi oil / o͝o book / o͞o boot / ou out / ŭ cut / û fur / *th* the / th thin
hw which / zh vision / ə ago, item, pencil, atom, circus

brass (brăs)   A yellowish metal made mostly of copper and zinc.

broad·en (**brôd′** n)   To make larger: *The workers broadened the narrow path to the seashore.*

bunt (bŭnt)   To push or bat something lightly so that it doesn't go far.

bur·row (**bûr′** ō)   **1.** A hole, tunnel, or opening dug in the ground by a small animal: *The rabbit hid in its burrow.*   **2.** To dig into: *The woodchuck will burrow into its hole.*

bus·tle (**bŭs′** əl)   To hurry and move around in a busy and excited way: *They were bustling about the house as they packed for the long vacation.*

byre (bīr)   A barn for cows.

C

cam·ou·flaged (**kăm′** ə fläzhd′)   Hidden or disguised by having the same colors or patterns of the surroundings: *The young rabbits were camouflaged by their brown fur.*

Can·dle·mas (**kăn′** dl məs)   A church celebration that takes place on February 2.

cel·e·brate (**sĕl′** ə brāt′)   To honor a special occasion by having a party or festival: *Rico celebrated his birthday last Tuesday.*

cel·lo (**chĕl′** ō)   A stringed instrument that is held between the knees when played. It is part of the violin family, but is larger than a violin and has a deeper tone.

clam·or (**klăm′** ər)   Loud noise: *I couldn't hear above the clamor of the crowd.*

col·lect (kə **lĕkt′**)   To get payment of: *He wanted to collect the money the woman owed him.*

com·fort (**kŭm′** fərt)   **1.** To soothe someone who is sad or frightened: *We tried to comfort the lost child.*   **2.** A state of well-being or ease: *It was a comfort to sit by the warm fire.*

com·pare (kəm **pâr′**)   To look at things to find out how they are alike or different: *We will compare prices before we decide which car to buy.*

con·sci·en·tious (kŏn′ shē **en′** shəs)   Done with care: *You have been very conscientious about doing your homework.*

con·ser·va·to·ry (kən **sûr′** və tôr′ ē) A special place in which plants are grown.

con·stant (**kŏn′** stənt) Happening all the time; without interruption: *He was bothered by the constant noise.*

con·tents (**kŏn′** tĕnts) Something that is inside a container: *We emptied the contents of the basket onto the floor.*

con·tin·ent (**kŏn′** tə nənt) One of the main land masses of the earth. The seven continents are Africa, Asia, Antarctica, Australia, Europe, North America, and South America.

con·trol (kən **trōl′**) **1.** To direct; to command. **2.** To hold back; to restrain: *I must try to control my temper.*

con·ven·ient (kən **vēn′** yənt) Easy to reach; handy.

con·ver·sa·tion (**kŏn′** vər **sā′** shən) Talk between two or more people.

cork (kôrk) A stopper for a bottle or a jug.

cour·age (**kûr′** ĭj) The quality that makes a person able to face danger or difficulty with bravery.

coy·o·te (kī **o′** tē) *or* (**kī′** ōt′) A wolflike animal.

crea·ture (**krē′** chər) A living being, especially an animal.

cur·i·ous (**kyŏor′** ē əs) **1.** Eager to find out or know about something: *We were curious about the new girl in our class.* **2.** Odd; rare: *A green elephant would be curious indeed!*

cur·rent (**kûr′** ənt) **1.** Water that is moving: *The current moved the boat.* **2.** Of the present time: *This is my current address.*

D

daw·dle (**dôd′** l) To take more time than you need: *I dawdled on the way to the market and got there after it had closed.*

debt (dĕt) Something that is owed: *We paid our debt to the bank.*

ă pat / ā pay / â care / ä father / ĕ pet / ē be / ĭ pit / ī pie / î fierce / ŏ pot / ō go
ô paw, for / oi oil / ŏŏ book / ōō boot / ou out / ŭ cut / û fur / *th* the / th thin
hw which / zh vision / ə ago, item, pencil, atom, circus

de·ceive (dĭ **sēv′**) To make a person believe something that is not true: *Was the thief deceiving the judge?*

def·i·nite (**dĕf′** ə nĭt) Certain; beyond doubt: *The letter said that my grandfather was definitely coming for a visit.*

def·i·ni·tion (dĕf ə **nĭsh′** ən) The meaning of a word or phrase: *One definition for the word* dive *is "to plunge headfirst into water."*

del·i·cate (**dĕl′** ĭ kĭt) Very finely made: *The dress was trimmed with delicate lace.*

de·li·cious (dĭ **lĭsh′** əs) Very pleasing to the taste or smell.

den (dĕn) The home of a wild animal.

de·ny (dĭ **nī′**) To declare that something is not true: *The man denied that he was a thief.*

de·pot (**dē′** pō) A railroad or bus station: *The man told me to wait for the bus at the depot.*

de·scrip·tion (dĭ **skrĭp′** shən) A statement that tells about something: *I recognized Alex's mother from his description of her.*

de·sert·ed (dĭ **zûrt′** əd) Without people: *It would be lonely to live on a deserted island.*

de·sign (dĭ **zīn′**) **1.** A pattern of lines, figures, or objects. **2.** To prepare a plan for something, especially by drawing.

des·o·late (**dĕs′** ə lĭt) **1.** Very unhappy; gloomy; without hope: *We were desolate when we lost the game by only one point.* **2.** Deserted: *The empty house looked desolate.*

des·per·ate (**dĕs′** pər ĭt) Without hope; willing to try anything because of the feeling of hopelessness: *I was desperate to find my lost homework.*

de·ter·mine (dĭ **tûr′** mĭn) To firmly decide or settle something: *I was determined to do well.*

di·a·ry (**dī′** ə rē) A record written each day of a person's own experiences.

di·rect·ly (dĭ **rĕkt′** lē) **1.** In a straight line or manner: *This road goes directly to the lake.* **2.** Soon; without delay: *I plan to go to the library directly after school.*

dis·cour·age (dĭ **skûr′** ĭj) To take away hope: *I was discouraged about my chances of making the team.*

dis·grace·ful (dĭs **grās′** fəl) Causing shame.

dis•guise (dĭs gīz′) **1.** Something that changes or hides a person's appearance. **2.** To change or hide one's identity.

dis•may (dĭs mā′) Sudden concern or discouragement when faced with difficulty: *Mike looked with dismay at the broken vase.*

dis•tance (dĭs′ təns) A stretch of space: *He travels a long distance to work each day.*

dis•tinct (dĭ stĭngkt′) Clear; unmistakable: *I distinctly remember turning off that light.*

dread (drĕd) Fear of something that might happen: *I thought about the next test with dread.*

drear•y (drîr′ ē) Gloomy, dull.

drift•wood (drĭft′ wŏŏd′) Wood that is floating on the water or that has been washed ashore.

due (dōō) *or* (dyōō) Owed: *I collected the money due me.*

dumb•found•ed (dŭm′ found′ əd) Speechless with surprise: *Alice was dumbfounded by the sight of the rocket liftoff.*

E

ea•ger (ē′ gər) Wanting something very much; very interested: *In her eagerness to catch the bus, she tripped.*

e•lec•tric•i•ty (ĭ lĕk trĭs′ ĭ tē) A form of energy: *Be sure to cut off the electricity by pulling the plug before you clean the toaster.*

em•bar•ras•sing (ĕm băr′ əs-ĭng) Causing an uneasy feeling: *I made an embarrassing spelling mistake.*

em•per•or (ĕm′ pər ər) A person who rules a group of countries.

ev•i•dence (ĕv′ ĭ dəns) Facts or signs that help one form an opinion: *The new evidence made the detective change his mind.*

ewe (yōō) A female sheep.

ex•am•ine (ĭg zăm′ ĭn) To look at closely and carefully.

ă pat / ā pay / â care / ä father / ĕ pet / ē be / ĭ pit / ī pie / î fierce / ŏ pot / ō go
ô paw, for / oi oil / ŏŏ book / ōō boot / ou out / ŭ cut / û fur / *th* the / th thin
hw which / zh vision / ə ago, item, pencil, atom, circus

ex·as·per·at·ed (ĭg zăs′ pə rāt′ əd) Annoyed; out of patience: *Ana became exasperated when there were so many changes in the plans.*

ex·er·cise (ĕk′ sər sīz′) **1.** Movement of the body to keep it fit: *My daily exercises keep my body feeling good.* **2.** To move the body to keep it fit: *I exercise every day.*

ex·plore (ĭk splôr′) To go to an unfamiliar place for the purpose of discovering something new: *Jack loved exploring the woods near his house.*

ex·pose (ĭk spōz′) To open to view; to leave uncovered or unprotected.

ex·tinct (ĭk stĭngkt′) Having died out: *Some kinds of birds have become extinct.*

F

fa·tal (fāt′ l) Causing death; very serious or important: *The mouse made a fatal mistake when it didn't run from the cat.*

fer·ret (fĕr′ ĭt) **1.** A small animal with yellowish fur that is related to the weasel. Ferrets are often trained to hunt rats or rabbits. **2.** To search; to hunt; to uncover: *The detective will ferret out the thief.*

fes·ti·val (fĕs′ tə vəl) A special day or time of celebration; a holiday.

flab·ber·gast·ed (flăb′ ərgăst′ ĭd) Surprised in a confused way: *Jane forgot that she had signed up for the race and was flabbergasted when she won.*

flaw·less (flô′ lĭs) Perfect.

flus·tered (flŭs′ tərd) Excited; confused: *Some people become flustered when they are asked too many questions.*

fond (fŏnd) Having a liking for: *He is fond of animals.*

for·bid·den (fər bĭd′ n) Not allowed; not permitted.

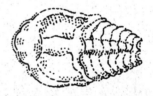

fos·sil (fŏs′ əl) A trace of a plant or animal that lived long ago. A fossil may be a footprint, the print of a skeleton, or the print of a leaf that remains in the hardened earth.

fran·ti·cal·ly (frăn′ tĭ kə lē) Excited with fear or worry: *Randy was searching frantically for his lost wallet.*

freight (frāt) Goods that are transported by a truck, train, ship, or other vehicle.

393

G

gale (gāl) A very strong wind.

gan·der (gǎn′ dər) A male goose.

gang·plank (gǎng′ plǎngk′) A ramp used for getting on and off a ship.

gen·er·a·tion (jĕn′ ə rā′ shən) A group of people born at around the same time. Children, parents, and grandparents form three different generations.

gloom·y (gloom′ ē) **1.** Sad. **2.** Causing sadness: *That gloomy movie made me feel sad.* **3.** Dark: *It wasn't sunny in the gloomy forest.*

glow·er (glou′ ər) To look at angrily; to scowl.

glum (glŭm) Sad; in low spirits; gloomy.

gnarled (närld) Rough, twisted, and full of knots: *The branches of the old apple tree are gnarled.*

grad·u·al·ly (grăj′ oo əl lē) Little by little; happening slowly.

grate·ful (grāt′ fəl) Feeling thankful: *She was grateful for the help of her neighbor.*

grieve (grēv) To feel great sadness; to mourn: *Debi grieved for her lost puppy.*

grove (grōv) A group of trees with open ground between them.

H

hard·ship (härd′ shĭp′) Something that causes difficulty or suffering.

har·mo·ny (här′ mə nē) **1.** A combination of individual parts to make up a pleasing whole: *Each flower contributed to the harmony of the garden.* **2.** Agreement; good will; peaceful relations: *My little brothers and sisters need to learn how to play together in harmony.*

ă pat / ā pay / â care / ä father / ĕ pet / ē be / ĭ pit / ī pie / î fierce / ŏ pot / ō go
ô paw, for / oi oil / oŏ book / oō boot / ou out / ŭ cut / û fur / *th* the / th thin
hw which / zh vision / ə ago, item, pencil, atom, circus

har·ness (här′ nĭs)   A set of leather straps and metal pieces by which an animal is attached to something, such as a cart.

har·vest (här′ vĭst)   The time when people gather in a crop.

ho·gan (hō′ gän)   A house made of logs and mud used by the Navajo Indians.

hol·low (hŏl′ ō)   **1.** Having a space or opening inside: *The tube is hollow.*   **2.** A small valley: *Let's meet down in the hollow.*

hon·est (ŏn′ ĭst)   Not lying, cheating, or stealing; able to be trusted.

hon·or (ŏn′ ər)   Good reputation; high standing with others: *My honor was saved when the witness agreed with my story.*

hon·or·ar·y (ŏn′ ə rĕr′ ē)   Given as an honor without having done the usual things for it: *Betty's picture wasn't good enough to win a real prize, but she worked so hard we gave her an honorary prize.*

hum·mock (hŭm′ ək)   A small, rounded hill.

I

i·den·ti·fi·ca·tion (ī dĕn′ tə fĭ kā′ shən)   The act of recognizing a particular person or thing.

i·mag·in·a·tion (ĭ măj′ ə nā′ shən)   The ability of the mind to create pictures of things that are not real or actually there; creativity: *That artist has a great imagination.*

i·mag·ine (ĭ măj′ ĭn)   To form a picture of something in the mind; to have an idea of: *I can imagine living in a castle.*

im·i·tate (ĭm′ ĭ tāt)   To copy the way someone acts: *The child was imitating the clown from the circus.*

im·me·di·ate·ly (ĭ mē′ dē ĭt lē)   Quickly; at once.

im·pa·tient (ĭm pā′ shənt)   Not able or willing to wait or put up with something calmly: *We waited impatiently for our friend who was late.*

im·per·i·al (ĭm pîr′ ē əl)   Having to do with an empire: *There were hundreds of cooks in the imperial kitchen.*

im·press (ĭm prĕs′) To have a strong effect on the feelings or mind: *I was impressed by the artist's skill.*

in·de·ci·sive (ĭn′ dĭ sī′ sĭv) Unable to make a judgment; unable to make up your mind: *Being indecisive can waste a lot of time.*

in·ge·nu·i·ty (ĭn′ jə no͞o′ ĭ tē) Skill in inventing or imagining things; cleverness: *His solution to the problem showed ingenuity.*

in·her·it (ĭn hĕr′ ĭt) To receive something from someone after he or she has died.

in·no·cent (ĭn′ ə sənt) Not guilty of a crime or wrongdoing: *The defendant looked at the jury innocently.*

in·quire (ĭn kwīr′) To ask about: *We inquired about the lost keys.*

in·sist (ĭn sĭst′) To state strongly: *He insisted that what he said was true.*

in·stinct (ĭn′ stĭngkt′) An inner feeling or way of behaving that is natural and not learned: *Cats seem to like to chase mice by instinct.*

in·ter·est rate (ĭn′ tə rĭst′ rāt) A charge for the use of borrowed money. Usually the interest is an additional percentage of the amount of money borrowed.

in·ter·rupt (ĭn′ tə rŭpt′) To hinder or stop someone or something by breaking in: *Our lesson was interrupted by the fire alarm.*

in·ter·view (ĭn′ tər vyo͞o′) To speak with someone to get information.

isle (īl) A very small island.

J

jas·mine (jăz′ mĭn) A vine or shrub with yellow or white flowers that smell very sweet.

joust (joust) A fight with lances between two knights on horseback.

ă pat / ā pay / â care / ä father / ĕ pet / ē be / ĭ pit / ī pie / î fierce / ŏ pot / ō go
ô paw, for / oi oil / o͝o book / o͞o boot / ou out / ŭ cut / û fur / *th* the / th thin
hw which / zh vision / ə ago, item, pencil, atom, circus

jut (jŭt) To stick upward or outward: *Branches jutted out from the trunk of the old tree.*

K

ka·ty·did (kā′ tē dĭd′) An insect that looks like a green grasshopper. It makes a shrill sound when it rubs its legs together.

knight (nīt) A soldier in the Middle Ages who served and pledged loyalty to a king or lord in return for the right to hold land.

L

lar·der (lär′ dər) A room or cupboard where food is stored.

ledg·er (lĕj′ ər) A book in which accounts of money received and spent are recorded.

loom (lōōm) 1. A machine or frame on which cloth is woven: *Marilee wove some blue cloth on the loom.* 2. To come into view, often seeming large or dangerous: *The stormclouds loomed in the distance.*

lulled (lŭld) Calmed and soothed: *The baby was lulled to sleep by the soft music.*

lum·ber (lŭm′ bər) 1. Wooden boards for building: *We used a lot of lumber to build the house.* 2. To move or walk in a clumsy, often noisy manner: *The elephants lumbered into the circus tent.*

lu·pine (lōō′ pĭn) A plant with clusters of different-colored flowers.

M

man·ger (mān′ jər) A trough or box that holds food for cattle or horses.

mare (mâr) A female horse.

ma·rine (mə rēn′) Relating to or having to do with the sea: *The whale is a marine animal.*

marsh (märsh) An area of very wet land; swamp: *They looked in the marsh for toads.*

mas·cot (măs′ kŏt′) *or* (măs′ kət) An animal or person believed to bring good luck.

mel·lowed (**mĕl′** ōd) Soft, rich, and soothing: *Andrew gazed at the mellowed colors of the old painting.*

me·sa (**mā′** sə) A hill with steep sides and a flat top.

mes·quite grass (mĕ **skēt′** grăs) Prairie grass that is like a thorny shrub called mesquite. Mesquite has feathery leaves and long, narrow pods.

met·al (**mĕt′** l) A shiny, hard material that can be melted and molded into shapes.

mi·gra·tion (mī **grā′** shən) A move from one place to another, often yearly.

mill (mĭl) **1.** A building where grain is ground into flour. **2.** A factory. **3.** To move around in a confused manner: *People milled about the auditorium before the show started.*

moist (moist) Slightly wet; damp: *Father cleaned off the table with a moist cloth.*

mon·i·tor (**mŏn′** ĭ tər) A student who does a special job to help a teacher in school.

mo·tion (**mō′** shən) **1.** A movement of a hand, arm, or other part of the body. **2.** To move a part of the body as a signal: *The horse seemed to motion to me with its head.*

mourn (môrn) *or* (mōrn) To feel or show sorrow for a death or loss: *She mourned the death of her pet.*

mus·cle (**mŭs′** əl) A kind of tissue in the body that can be tightened or relaxed to make body parts move.

mus·sel (**mŭs′** əl) A water animal with a soft body and a pair of narrow, dark-blue shells.

mus·tang (**mŭs′** tăng′) A small wild horse.

O

ob·vi·ous (**ŏb′** vē əs) Easily seen or understood: *The coat was obviously old and worn.*

or·chard (**ôr′** chərd) A plot of land where fruit trees are grown.

ă pat / ā pay / â care / ä father / ĕ pet / ē be / ĭ pit / ī pie / î fierce / ŏ pot / ō go
ô paw, for / oi oil / o͝o book / o͞o boot / ou out / ŭ cut / û fur / *th* the / th thin
hw which / zh vision / ə ago, item, pencil, atom, circus

o·rig·i·nal (ə **rĭj′** ə nəl)   The first; not copied: *We have an original painting by a famous artist.*

os·trich (**ŏs′** trĭch)   A large African bird with long legs and neck. It cannot fly but can run very fast.

owe (ō)   To have to pay: *How much do you owe for your lunch?*

oy·ster (**oi′** stər)   A sea animal that has a soft body and a rough, uneven shell with two parts.

P

par·tial (**pär′** shəl)   Having a special liking for: *I'm partial to skiing.*

par·tic·u·lar (pər **tĭk′** yə lər)   Different from the others: *On that particular day I was sick.*

pas·sen·ger (**păs′** ən jər)   A person who is riding in a vehicle.

pass·port (**păs′** pôrt′) *or* (**păs′** pōrt)   A small book that identifies a person who is traveling from one country to another: *I had to get a passport for my trip to China and Japan.*

pas·ture (**păs′** chər)   **1.** Land where animals graze.   **2.** To herd animals to a certain area to graze.

peas·ant (**pĕz′** ənt)   A term used in Europe for person who works on a small farm.

pen·guin (**pĕn′** gwĭn) *or* (**pĕng′** gwĭn)   A sea bird with webbed feet and small wings that cannot fly. Penguins live near Antarctica.

pen·man·ship (**pĕn′** mən shĭp′)   The skill or style of writing.

per·sist (pər **sĭst′**)   To continue to say or do something again and again: *The child persisted in teasing her sister.*

per·suade (pər **swād′**)   To convince someone to do or believe something: *We persuaded the children to play more quietly.*

pierce (pîrs)   To go into or through: *The sound of laughter pierced the silence.*

pit·i·ful (**pĭt′** ĭ fəl)   Arousing sorrow, pity, and sympathy. *The young boy cried pitifully when his parents left him.*

plunge (plŭnj)   To throw oneself into the water, a place, or an activity: *They plunged into the sea.*

por·ridge (pôr′ ĭj)   A thick cereal or soup that is made by boiling oatmeal or other grains in milk or water.

pose (pōz)   To take a special position: *The family posed on the front steps.*

pos·i·tive (pŏz′ ĭ tĭv)   Absolutely certain: *They had positive proof that he stole the money.*

pos·ture (pŏs′ chər)   The way a person holds and carries the body: *That dancer has beautiful posture.*

pre·serve (prĭ zûrv′)   To keep in the same form: *The plants were preserved in perfect form.*

pro·clam·a·tion (prŏk′ lə mā′ shən)   Announcement.

prompt·ly (prŏmpt′ lē)   **1.** Without delay; at once: *You left promptly when John arrived.* **2.** At the proper time: *I get to school promptly at 8:00 every day.*

pro·per·ly (prŏp′ ər lē)   In the correct manner: *She didn't tie her shoes properly.*

pro·tect (prə tĕkt′)   To keep from harm or danger.

pro·test (prə tĕst′)   To complain or object: *Our class will protest the new rule.*

Q

quar·ry (kwôr′ ē)   A deep, open place where stone is taken out by cutting or blasting.

R

ran·som (răn′ səm)   Money that is paid or demanded so that a person who is held prisoner will be set free.

rare (râr)   **1.** Not found or seen very often; uncommon. **2.** Special; having a high value: *My uncle collects rare books.*

reap (rēp)   To harvest a crop: *The farmers reaped the grain.*

reg·u·la·tion (rĕg′ yə lā′ shən)   Rule.

re·la·tion (rĭ lā′ shən)   A person who belongs to the same family; a relative: *We invited all our friends and relations to the party.*

ă pat / ā pay / â care / ä father / ĕ pet / ē be / ĭ pit / ī pie / î fierce / ŏ pot / ō go
ô paw, for / oi oil / ŏŏ book / ōō boot / ou out / ŭ cut / û fur / *th* the / th thin
hw which / zh vision / ə ago, item, pencil, atom, circus

rel·a·tive (**rĕl′** ə tĭv)   A person who belongs to the same family; a person related to another.

re·quest (rĭ **kwĕst′**)   Something that is asked for.

res·cue (**rĕs′** kyōo)   To save from danger.

re·search (rĭ **sûrch′**) *or* (**rē′** sûrch)   The carefully planned study of a subject.

re·sent (rĭ **zĕnt′**)   To feel angry about: *The boy resented the teasing of his classmates.*

re·spect·ful (rĭ **spĕkt′** fəl)   Showing proper consideration and honor: *Maria respectfully opened the door for her grandmother.*

re·store (rĭ **stôr′**)   To bring back to the original condition: *Water and plant food helped restore the plant.*

re·sult (rĭ **zŭlt′**)   Something that happens because of something else: *The lack of trees is a result of last year's tornado.*

rhyth·mic (**rĭth′** mĭk)   Having a regular pattern of movement, action, or sounds: *I like to hear the rhythmic sound of drums.*

rig·id (**rĭj′** ĭd)   Not bending; stiff: *The soldiers remained rigid during the drill.*

roy·al (**roi′** əl)   Belonging to or serving a king or queen: *There is a party at the royal palace.*

rub·ble (**rŭb′** əl)   Pieces of broken stone or other material: *Machines cleared the rubble after the building was torn down.*

S

sap·ling (**săp′** lĭng)   A young tree: *I planted a sapling.*

sat·is·fac·to·ry (săt′ ĭs **făk′** tə rē)   Good enough but not excellent: *My grades were satisfactory, but they could have been better.*

sat·is·fac·tion (săt′ ĭs **făk′**shən)   Pleasure that comes from the fulfillment of something.

sat·is·fy (**săt′** ĭs fī′)   To have enough to fulfill a need or desire: *I was satisfied with my grade on the test.*

sa•vor•y (**sā′** vər ē)   Tasting or smelling delicious: *The savory smell of the soup greeted us when we opened the kitchen door.*

scold (skōld)   To yell at or speak angrily to: *I scolded my dog after it chewed my shoes.*

scone (skōn)   A small, biscuit-like bread: *We ate scones for breakfast.*

scorn•ful•ly (**skôrn′** fəl ē)   In a manner that looks down on someone or something.

scroll (skrōl)   A roll of fine parchment or paper on which something is written.

sculp•ture (**skŭlp′** chər)   A work of art made by shaping figures or designs in wood, clay, or metal.

se•cure (sĭ **kyoŏr′**)   Tight or strong: *She tied the knot securely so that it wouldn't come untied.*

sel•dom (**sĕl′** dəm)   Not often.

sep•a•rate (**sĕp′** ə rāt′)   **1.** To divide into different parts or sections.   **2.** To put or pull apart: *She separated the ribbons so that she could give one to each child.*

se•ri•ous (**sîr′** ē əs)   Solemn; not joking: *He had a serious expression on his face when he told her the bad news.*

sham•bles (**shăm′** bəlz)   Disorder.

shel•lac (shə **lăk′**)   A hard varnish that is used to protect the surface of something.

shel•ter (**shĕl′** tər)   Something that protects or covers: *During the storm, we stayed in the shelter on the mountain.*

short•bread (**shôrt′** brĕd′)   A dough made of flour, sugar, and butter that is cut into a thin cake or cookies and then baked.

shriv•el (**shrĭv′** əl)   To make or to become smaller and wrinkled; to wither: *Those plants will shrivel in the hot sun.*

ă pat / ā **pay** / â care / ä father / ĕ **pet** / ē be / ĭ **pit** / ī **pie** / î **fie**rce / ŏ **pot** / ō go
ô paw, for / oi **oi**l / oŏ **boo**k / o͞o **boo**t / ou **out** / ŭ **cut** / û **fur** / *th* **the** / th **thin**
hw **wh**ich / zh vision / ə **a**go, it**e**m, penc**i**l, at**o**m, circ**u**s

si·lence (**sī′** ləns) No sound or noise: *There was silence in the room.*

site (sīt) Location; place: *We will build the house on this site.*

sleet (slēt) Partly frozen rain.

sliv·er (**slĭv′** ər) A thin, sharp piece of wood, glass, or other material; a splinter.

sol·emn (**sŏl′** əm) Serious; grave.

sow (sō) To scatter or plant to produce a crop: *The farmer was sowing corn in one of the fields.*

spir·its (**spĭr′** ĭts) A person's mood or state of mind: *Though he was ill, he was in good spirits.*

splen·did (**splĕn′** dĭd) **1.** Very beautiful: *The sunset was splendid.* **2.** Excellent or fine: *What a splendid idea!*

sta·ble (**stā′** bəl) A building that shelters animals such as horses.

stal·lion (**stăl′** yən) A male horse that is fully grown.

stam·pede (stăm **pēd′**) A sudden, violent rush of animals, such as horses, cattle, or buffalo.

stern·ly (**stûrn′** lē) In a firm way: *The teacher spoke sternly to the noisy class.*

stout·ness (**stout′** nĭs) The quality of being large or fat.

sug·ges·tion (səg **jĕs′** chən) Something that is brought up for consideration.

sus·pect (sə **spĕkt′**) To think that someone may be guilty without having proof; distrust.

sus·tain (sə **stān′**) To keep up the spirits; to support: *Our friendship sustained us in times of trouble.*

swift (swĭft) Moving or able to move very quickly: *The birds flew swiftly out of sight.*

T

tal·on (**tăl′** ən) The claw of a bird, such as an owl or eagle, that catches other animals as prey.

tang·y (**tăng′** ē) Having a strong, sharp taste: *Have a glass of this tangy lemonade.*

temp·er·a·ment·al (**tĕm′** prə **mĕn′** tl) Moody; irritable; changeable.

thor·ough·ly (**thûr′** ō lē) Completely; fully: *His shoes were thoroughly soaked after he walked in the puddle.*

tis·sue (tĭsh′ ōō) Light, thin paper that is often used for wrapping.

to·ken (tō′ kən) Something that stands as a sign for something else: *Belinda gave me her scarf as a token of our friendship.*

tour·na·ment (tōor′ nə mənt) *or* (tûr′ nə mənt) In the Middle Ages, a contest among many jousting knights.

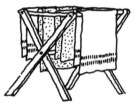

tow·el-horse (tou′ əl hôrs′) A rack for holding towels.

trans·form (trăns fôrm′) To change greatly in form or appearance: *For the party, the hall was transformed into a magic kingdom.*

trop·i·cal (trŏp′ ĭ kəl) **1.** Of, like, or found in the areas of the earth that are near the equator: *We took a trip to a tropical island.* **2.** Hot and humid.

tum·ble·weed (tŭm′ bəl wēd′) A plant that breaks off when it is dry and rolls about in the wind.

U

un·pleas·ant (ŭn plĕz′ ənt) Not pleasing; not agreeable: *She spoke to the noisy children in an unpleasant way.*

un·rav·el (ŭn răv′ əl) To undo something that is knitted: *My sweater got caught on a nail and began unraveling.*

ur·gent (ûr′ jənt) Needing quick attention: *Read the message right away, because it's urgent!*

V

val·u·a·ble (văl′ yōō ə bəl) Worth a great deal.

W

warp (wôrp) Threads of yarn attached to a loom from top to bottom. Other threads are woven in and out of the warp. (See the picture for *loom*.)

ă pat / ā pay / â care / ä father / ĕ pet / ē be / ĭ pit / ī pie / î fierce / ŏ pot / ō go
ô paw, for / oi oil / ŏŏ book / ōō boot / ou out / ŭ cut / û fur / *th* the / th thin
hw which / zh vision / ə ago, item, pencil, atom, circus

wealth·y (wĕl′ thē) Having a great amount of money or possessions; rich.

weft (wĕft) Threads of yarn that are woven crosswise, in and out of the warp yarns. (See the picture for *loom*.)

whim (hwĭm) A sudden wish or idea: *We decided to go to the party on a whim.*

whip·poor·will (hwĭp′ ər wĭl′) A plump, brownish bird that has a call that sounds like its name.

wilt (wĭlt) To lose freshness; to become limp; to droop: *The flowers in the vase wilted after only one day.*

wis·dom (wĭz′ dəm) Good judgment in knowing what to do and what is good, bad, right, and wrong: *A person may gain wisdom through experience.*

wit (wĭt) The ability to think clearly: *You need to have a sharp wit to understand her jokes.*

wob·ble (wŏb′ əl) To move unsteadily from side to side: *The legs of the chair were so loose that it wobbled back and forth.*

wob·bly (wŏb′ lē) Unsteady: *The broken table was so wobbly that we couldn't put the plates on it.*

Credits